# The Devil's Bride

by

## MARGARET PARGETER

D0188544

# *Harlequin Books*

TORONTO · LONDON · NEW YORK · AMSTERDAM
SYDNEY · HAMBURG · PARIS · STOCKHOLM

Original hardcover edition published 1979
by Mills & Boon Limited

ISBN 0-373-02296-4

Harlequin edition published in November 1979

Printed in U.S.A

# CHAPTER ONE

'WHAT you ask is out of the question, of course.' Sandra, short for Alexandra, Weir spoke slowly but distinctly, the calmness of her clear young voice belied somewhat by the expression of startled amazement in her wide green eyes as she gazed blankly at her cousin. 'You're suggesting I take your place, pretend to be the fiancée of a man who can't see? Why, you must be mad to even think I would do such a thing!'

'Well, I am suggesting it!' Sandra's cousin, who was known as Alexandra, as she had been named first, stared back at her dispassionately, her thin brows lifting. 'You always were too impulsive, my dear. If you'll just hear me out you might realise that my crazy idea could actually be the solution to all your problems. About the only solution, so far as I can see.'

Heedlessly Sandra interrupted, not prepared at this stage to admit the enormity of her problems. Certainly the fix she was in was entirely her own business, unfortunate as this might be. Angrily she asked, 'Whatever made you think of me?'

'Several things.' The girl opposite spoke with a coolness Sandra envied. She even paused to yawn delicately behind long, elegant fingers, as if the whole traumatic situation merely bored her, as did the necessity of having to visit this shabby, old-fashioned cottage in such a quiet country village. Her veiled glance played idly over Sandra's shocked face before she went on, 'Quite frankly I was in a jam and already looking for a solution when I heard of Gran's death, but it wasn't until I was told we'd each been left

5

a hundred pounds that I decided to come and see you. I mean,' she excused herself neatly as Sandra's expression changed to one of disgust, 'there didn't seem much point in visiting Gran these last few years. She never approved of me, especially after I went in for modelling. One would have thought I was in league with the devil!'

'Alexandra, please!'

'Oh, all right! I suppose Gran's opinion can't matter any more so, as you're so clearly getting impatient, I'll get back to all this money she left. A hundred pounds! I estimated, even used carefully, that it would scarcely keep you more than two or three weeks, and before long you were going to find yourself destitute. Then, although you might not immediately follow, we both have the same christian and surnames. It seems rather ludicrous that we were both named Alexandra by parents who fondly imagined this would lead to our inheriting Gran's fortune. The fortune she so stupidly lost through foolish investment!'

'It wasn't altogether Gran's fault,' Sandra cut in hotly.

'Okay, keep your hair on!' her cousin exclaimed crudely. 'Anyway, it seems a bit late to debate the point now. Possibly, in spite of the fact that she died leaving you practically nothing, you might still have something to thank her for. Our names being the same, for instance, simplifies everything regarding passports and such. That Stein calls me Alexandra is neither here nor there. I'm sure he would be quite willing to shorten it to Sandra, if you found it confusing. He considers Alexandra too much of a mouthful anyway, so this should be no problem, if you consent to taking my place.'

Sandra ignored this. It seemed too wildly incredible even to contemplate. 'You can't realise what you're saying,' she gasped, rising, in her agitation, to poke the fire for which she had little fuel left. 'Why can't you just tell Stein frankly you want to marry another man? I don't know him, but you did once send Gran his photograph. I'm sure a man who looks as arrogant as he does would be able to take it, whether he can see or not!'

'That's just it,' Alexandra frowned quickly. 'I'm not sure he can. He's young enough, still in his thirties, to be able to face most things without going under, but lately he's been rather peculiar in a terse, bad-tempered sort of way. It's not so long since his accident, so I expect he hasn't really had time to adjust, not properly. His doctor says his nerves aren't too good, not as good, anyway, as Stein would have people believe, and I must be extra careful. This is why I feel I can't take any risks by springing my change of heart on him suddenly.'

'But if this other man you want to marry, this Arnold, really loves you, wouldn't he be prepared to wait?'

'No!' For the first time since she had arrived Alexandra appeared agitated. 'Arnold does love me and I mean to have him. I can't help wondering, though, should Stein be driven to doing something desperate because of me, if Arnold's love would stand the test? He may be a millionaire, or almost, but he has an absolute abhorrence of scandal. I would lose him for sure!'

'But if Stein only wants you to spend a few weeks with him on this Greek island to see if you can really put up with his blindness, doesn't this suggest he has doubts himself? About your future relationship, I mean?'

'I don't know.' Alexandra sounded curiously reluctant to discuss this question any more than she had done. 'The thing is that though I still think Stein adores me, we weren't all that compatible even before his accident. Not that,' her laughter rang out, brittle and confident, 'we wouldn't have been all right if it hadn't happened, but unfortunately one can never put back the clock. You must believe Arnold won't hear of me going off with Stein, no matter what the circumstances. He's quite willing to give you five thousand or more to take my place, to break it to Stein gently, but he quite frankly declares if I go myself he's finished!'

Sandra blinked, struggling to free herself from a maze of contempt. 'Arnold surely can't love you very much if he doesn't trust you?'

Her cousin's face changed bitterly, 'I think it's Stein he doesn't trust. One only has to look at him to see that even blind he's still quite a man.'

Sandra's breath caught painfully in her slender throat and for one moment she was tempted to capitulate. One half of her was enthralled by the exciting dark image of a man whose likeness she had held in her heart for a long time, the other half, her conventional, unawakened half, appalled. Shivering but unable to restrain herself, she asked, 'If I went with Stein Freeman to this island how can you be sure he would be willing to let me go? An island can't be the easiest place to escape from.'

'I can promise Stein would never keep anyone against their will. He has too much pride for that.' Alexandra sounded cynical, but she moved so restlessly that instinctively Sandra knew she wasn't going to hear the whole truth. 'We've had rather an unusual engagement,' Alexandra continued. 'I had a small part when they were filming his latest book. It was the first part I'd ever managed to get and you've no idea how wonderful I felt. Unfortunately the assistant producer took a fancy to me and the great fat slob couldn't seem to understand why I didn't fancy him! This was when Stein came to my rescue. He more or less took me over. I've always maintained a few tears never came amiss. Actually I think Stein had his own personal problems just then, though what they were exactly he never told me, but perhaps this made him more sympathetic towards mine. He suggested, eventually, that it might be a good idea to become engaged.'

'Didn't he love you? Was his offer simply to protect you?'

'No!' Alexandra protested angrily. 'Of course he loves me—this is why I'm so afraid. Too scared of the consequences to just walk out on him.'

Sandra stared at her frowning, trying in vain to sort it all out. Her beautiful, sophisticated cousin more than confused her. 'Did you stop loving him after he was blinded?'

The flush that mounted Alexandra's face was vindictive. 'You always did try to show me in a bad light, didn't you, Sandra!' Then, as if realising she couldn't afford to offend, she muttered a reluctant apology. 'To tell you the truth,' she said ruefully, 'I don't think I ever loved Stein all that much. Certainly I couldn't give him the depth of passion he sometimes seemed to expect. Once I remember him saying—I thought sarcastically—that if a woman couldn't be generous with her heart there was always her body.'

Sandra's traitorous pulse jumped fearfully, 'What did you say to that?'

'Trust you to want to know! Already you have a much more sensuous look about you than I'll ever have. If Stein could only see I'm sure he would appreciate it!' Alexandra's hard laughter rang. 'I didn't tell him I'd never cared for that sort of thing. I simply pretended I was keeping myself for marriage. Naturally I didn't want him to think me frigid as he was, still is I suppose, an extremely good catch.'

'Yet now you think Arnold might be even better?' Sandra couldn't keep the coldness from her voice.

Alexandra, however, seemed not to notice, so absorbed was she in herself. 'Arnold's everything in a man I've ever dreamt of. He's much more malleable than Stein. Neither is he so physical, if you know what I mean?'

Alexandra wouldn't care for that, Sandra knew. Curiously she wondered if either Stein Freeman or Arnold had guessed at Alexandra's coldness when they'd talked of marriage. She said hesitantly, 'I still can't understand how you can contemplate deserting Stein like this, no matter what Arnold's attractions.'

Seeing Sandra's contemptuous expression, Alexandra retorted harshly, 'I do wish you'd take that self-righteous look off your face and try to understand. I'm a model, used to having men appreciate me. I simply couldn't face a

future tied to a man who couldn't see me. I think it was
only my beauty that appealed to Stein—now he can't see
me any more it's rather like being engaged to a stranger!
He very rarely so much as tries to kiss me nowadays, and,
when he does, there doesn't seem to be anything between
us. You're only twenty-one, Sandra, eight years younger
than I am, so you can't realise how time is important. My
chances of making a good marriage can only get slimmer.'

This made no sense to Sandra, but she remained silent
as Alexandra sneered, 'It's pretty obvious you don't think
I'm justified, but there's Stein's work too, you see.'

'His work?' Sandra repeated blankly.

'Yes,' Alexandra's thin lips curled. 'He used to do most
of his own typing. Now it's suddenly occurred to him that
he won't be able to continue without a secretary. Actually
he's already had three from an agency, but each one left in
tears. So he insists I must help him. Me!' Dramatically,
her pale eyes widening, she held up her hands. 'I can't even
use two fingers properly, and he suggests I practise! This
is where you would fit in nicely, as haven't you already
worked part time for a writer at the other end of the village,
before he went abroad? Gran told me about it once, when
she wrote.'

'But I was never properly trained.' Startled, Sandra
spoke hastily. 'I just did it to try and earn a little money
while I looked after Gran. To begin with I don't suppose
I was any better than you. You could easily learn to work
with a writer. Mr Lawrence said I caught on very quickly
and didn't obtrude.'

Alexandra grimaced unkindly. 'That's understandable,
my dear, as you're so young and retiring. I'm not trying to
be deliberately cruel,' she added, as Sandra's cheeks went
pink, 'but, as I'm a model, men find me distracting.'

'But Stein can't see you?'

'That's half the trouble,' Alexandra grumbled. 'Now
he can't see me it's as if he were looking for a mind, rather

than a body, and it's just not on, not as far as I'm concerned.'

This, Sandra guessed, with sudden clarity, was where her cousin would fail. Alexandra was crafty rather than intelligent, though people rarely saw the difference. She had also a kind of superficial gaiety which relied a lot on rather exaggerated facial expression. Sandra could see how a man with Stein Freeman's disability might find himself groping after something which had only been an illusion. It could be dreadful for him to discover that the Alexandra he sought simply did not exist!

Yet for Alexandra to suggest she might take her place was plainly ridiculous. It could border on insanity to consider it, even if it was possible. 'I couldn't do it,' she heard herself whispering fearfully, while feeling herself torn desperately with compassion. Not just for Stein Freeman, she mentally corrected herself warily, for any man in such tragic circumstances. 'I still couldn't do it,' she reiterated, distractedly.

Sharply, her eyes fixed comprehendingly on her cousin's disturbed face, Alexandra prepared to take every advantage. 'I think,' she said smoothly, 'if you take a good look at your present situation you'll find you haven't much choice. You've looked after Gran since you left school. Now you're left with scarcely a penny in a house which the owner wants to sell, but which you couldn't afford to live in even if you were able to—not with the unemployment position regarding untrained girls the way it is. And if you couldn't make ends meet here, how long do you think you'd last in London?'

'I don't know.' Sandra went white, her green eyes haunted. Alexandra was only putting into words problems she had been worrying over for days. To bring them out into the open seemed only to emphasise them!

'You'd probably starve,' Alexandra retorted bluntly. 'Even if you're fully trained it's not easy to find anything.

If you went with Stein to Kalnos it would give you time to decide exactly what you want to do, and then you would have Arnold's money to help you train.'

Nervously Sandra clenched her hands. She didn't want to look at her cousin, hating her as she did for putting temptation in her way. But the biggest temptation, she realised, was Stein himself. Ever since Alexandra had sent his photograph he had come between Sandra and everything she did. This, if she could have taken it, might have been a chance to get rid of a foolish infatuation, because that was all it could amount to! One didn't fall in love with a photograph, however attractive. When Alexandra had first told her of Stein's accident, the irreparable damage to the optic nerve, Sandra had almost wept, feeling, as she had done, the pain of his affliction in her own eyes and heart. She had felt a deep pity, an urgent need to give him comfort, but she wasn't naïve enough to imagine he would welcome either her or her pity. It was Alexandra he naturally wanted.

'Are you listening?' Alexandra asked coldly.

'Yes,' Sandra returned dully. Suddenly, recklessly, she cried, 'I'll admit to feeling tempted. In my position,' she laughed bitterly, 'who wouldn't, but what you suggest is so impractical I doubt if it would ever work. I know one reads of this kind of situation, but there's a vast difference between real life and fiction. How would I know, for instance, what kind of man Stein really is? How he reacts to situations? I'm not only a total stranger, I'm younger and not so smart as you, as you've already pointed out.'

Alexandra stirred cautiously, as if sensing that which she had hoped for was almost within her grasp. 'In many ways,' she said dryly, 'Stein is still something of a stranger to me, so I don't think this would present much of a problem. 'I'm older than you, but because of my career I've kept slim. Our height and weight must be about the same, although your curves are more pronounced. You just wouldn't have to get too near him, that's all. I'll admit that otherwise we don't look alike, but a blind man wouldn't see that your eyes are a different colour and your mouth too sensuous for your own good.' Alexandra's eyes were full of light mockery. 'Poor Stein, what a shame he won't know what he's missing!'

Sandra gasped, her cheeks hot, 'My hair isn't quite so fair.

Alexandra merely shrugged. 'Stein is perfectly aware that I have mine tinted. If anyone should point this out he would simply conclude that I don't any more. I'll not deny I haven't your look of young innocence, or that my skin has no longer the satiny texture of yours, but a blind man, my dear, is scarcely likely to notice.'

Sandra winced. For a moment Alexandra had sounded almost cruel. 'My voice?' she whispered, trying to ignore Alexandra's hardness along with a growing conviction that every question she asked was getting more incredibly stupid!

'Your voice?' Alexandra smiled brightly. 'Oh, I don't think you need worry about that. After all, we both come from the same kind of family and went to the same school. I suppose with Gran being so ill for so long you've had to learn to tone yours down, but I will, over the next few days, endeavour to speak softly to Stein. Don't forget, my dear child, that as well as being a model I've had some acting experience.'

'I think I'm going to need that more than you.' As she realised what she had just said, Sandra's face paled. She said quickly, 'That doesn't mean I agree to do as you ask— I still think it would be crazy. Stein would be sure to find out. I've read somewhere that blind people develop a great sensitivity.'

'Stein has scarcely had time.'

Sandra tried to ignore Alexandra's reassuring purr.

'Stein's accident,' even to ask seemed actually to hurt her in some strange way, 'how did it happen?'

'Glass from his windscreen. A head-on collision with a drunken motorist.' Alexandra, as usual, had a dislike of gory details and kept her answers brief.

Sandra felt herself tremble as if she could see it happen. She could feel the horror and the pain moving through her as if she had almost been part of it. How could Alexandra be willing to turn her back on a man who had gone through all that? It seemed too heartless an act even to contemplate. Someone, somehow, must try to make it up to him. Only surely this couldn't mean herself! Yet, if she continued to refuse, would this make her any better than Alexandra? Money didn't come into it. Sandra's heart overflowed with compassion.

'Poor Stein,' she murmured, feeling the words totally inadequate.

'The thing is,' Alexandra shrugged, 'without his eyesight he could end up that way!'

Aghast at her cousin's indifference, Sandra exclaimed, 'And it wouldn't suit you to be tied to a man without a penny to his name?'

'There's no need to be so disparaging.' Petulantly Alexandra rose to her elegantly shod feet. Restlessly she wandered over the shabby, rose-strewn carpet of her grandmother's sitting room. 'I was never made to thrive on poverty, as you appear to have done,' she sneered. 'Besides, I should moulder away on a Greek Island.'

'Haven't you tried to explain this to Stein?' Sandra asked reasonably. 'Perhaps he doesn't realise?'

'You'd think he would! Even a few weeks without any regular form of entertainment! He seems to imagine I should be able to exist on love!'

'On love?' Sandra gulped quickly as her throat went tight. 'I thought you said he didn't talk of it any more?'

'Oh, take no notice of that!' Just as swiftly Alexandra

grimaced. 'It's merely the Greek in him. Naturally they discuss love as we would eggs and bacon.'

'You didn't say anything about his being Greek!' Sandra couldn't restrain her low note of accusation.

'He's not Greek!' Alexandra's thin mouth firmed in exasperation. 'It's just his grandmother who is. He's as English as you and me. I'm sure you have nothing to fear.'

But instinctively Sandra felt she had, if only Alexandra would give her time to think. Even if Stein Freeman had just a little Greek blood in his veins it would make him a man to be reckoned with. Wasn't it well known that the Greeks believed in a stringent code of conduct? With cold fingers of fright curling around her fast beating heart she cried, 'The whole thing is ridiculous! I couldn't possibly do it.'

'Very well.' For a moment Alexandra's face was venomous as she said smoothly, 'If you won't you won't. All I hope is that you don't expect me to help you or even see you again after this. I'll tell Stein, as you advise, and if he jumps in the river, he'll just have to!'

'Oh, no!' the horror in Sandra's voice was clearly audible. 'You simply can't, Alexandra!'

'I can and I will!' Alexandra turned on her with a fury so unstable as to be absolutely convincing. 'You can't stop me, but you can stop judging me like a sanctimonious little saint!'

For a long moment there was silence as the two cousins stood regarding each other. Sandra was aware of the hate on Alexandra's face, but it wasn't this that made her look away first. 'All right,' she agreed, feeling driven by some inner compulsion which, against all her more cautious instincts, would allow no other reply, 'if you're sure I can do it?'

'I'm sure,' Alexandra nodded, with a hint of smug satisfaction that Sandra scarcely noticed.

'Perhaps, as you say,' Sandra shrugged, trying desperately to stiffen her wavering decision, 'it will help Stein—and what have I to lose?'

A few days later, on her way to London, Sandra was still wondering just how true her rash statement would prove to be. Alexandra, she realised, had outwitted her, Alexandra and Stein Freeman between them. The willpower of one, the hard masculine attraction of the other, this and the plight Stein was in. Carefully she tried to channel her shaken feelings on to a more impersonal plane, rather than think about it as she had been doing constantly since Alexandra had left. Couldn't this be a chance of adventure, a change of scene such as had never come her way before, or was likely to come again? Never, until now, had there been a chance of spreading her wings. How could there have been when she had to nurse an ailing grandmother almost continually since she had left school. Apart from Alexandra's brief visits there had been no one else.

Quickly Sandra bit back a sobbing breath, not of self-pity but apprehension. Alexandra had led such a very different sort of life. It wouldn't have occurred to her that after various unavoidable expenses had been met there was very little of Sandra's hundred pounds left. Sentiment apart, this proposition of Alexandra's seemed, when Sandra had really got down to considering it, the only possible way out. God knows she regretted it bitterly, but hadn't she tried every other alternative without success? If Stein Freeman did find out about her deception he could be no worse off, surely, than he might be if Alexandra deserted him now and left him with no one. Sandra knew she must keep thinking along these lines in order to retain her sanity.

Burying her small face in a magazine she didn't really see, she groped hopelessly with her ensuing problems. Unlike Alexandra she was no actress. How did one suddenly take over the role of a man's fiancée? How could she walk into his flat and talk to him as if she was quite used to doing such a thing? Already she was bitterly regretting the promise she had made to Alexandra. It had been easy enough to memorise most of the things Alexandra had told her, and she had told her enough during the two days she had spent with her, but how could anyone guarantee that the whole thing wouldn't turn out an absolute fiasco?

Fortunately there seemed no immediate snags as Stein had just returned from America and none of his English friends had yet met Alexandra. He was living in a service flat with which he had been quickly familiar and in another few days he would be in Greece where he had enough servants, should he need them. Even his regular physician was off on holiday, so there would be no problem there.

'Don't you see, it's as if fate was on my side,' Alexandra laughed triumphantly when Sandra arrived at her flat. 'You've got here safely and no one is going to suspect a thing.'

That was one hurdle, Sandra admitted, while suspecting there would be other, more dangerous ones to face. Almost before she had set her suitcase down in Alexandra's small bedroom which they were apparently to share, Alexandra was telling her she would need some new clothes.

'But if Stein can't see,' Sandra protested, 'what's the point?'

'The point is,' Alexandra said tersely, 'he knows the quality of mine by touch. Touch seems to be important to him. That's another thing,' her elegant nose wrinkled distastefully. 'You know how I hate being pawed.'

As Sandra stared at her uneasily, a twinge of fear flicking her, Alexandra glanced at her swiftly. 'It's just the usual kind of thing, you know. Taking my coat, my arm occasionally. Nothing more.'

'I see.' Sandra glanced around her uncertainly, wishing fervently she could be back in her old village home with only Gran to worry about. 'About clothes,' she began.

'Don't worry about that.' Alexandra took her arm, leading her back into the lounge. 'There are several things of mine which will be suitable, I think. The rest I'll buy you, as a present if you like. After all, I'm not going to be short of a bob or two, not after I'm married. No one need know, least of all Arnold.'

The whole of the next day was devoted to rigging Sandra out in what Alexandra considered suitable clothing and familiarising her with the immediate district. 'Not that it matters much,' Alexandra said. 'By the end of the week we will both be gone, but it's essential that you know your way around, if only for a few days. Actually my flat and everything is paid up until the end of the week. All there remains to do is to hand the keys in to the caretaker.'

Afterwards Sandra wondered why this didn't warn her as to Alexandra's real intentions, but her thoughts were so full of the ordeal in front of her that no suspicion crossed her mind. The next evening, when she was to visit Stein for the first time, her nerves were so taut she doubted if she could go through with it.

'I don't think I can,' she exclaimed, white-faced. 'I think if you'd just let me go and explain frankly why you want to end your engagement, Stein would understand. Nothing could be as bad as this deliberate plan to deceive him. No one would believe such a situation could exist!'

'Don't you see, you little fool, that's exactly what I'm banking on!' Alexandra's hiss was suddenly vicious, 'Goodness knows I've spent long enough cramming you up. I refuse to have you let me down at the last minute.'

Swiftly Alexandra hustled her into her dress, refusing to give her another chance to protest as she rang for a taxi. It wasn't until it arrived that she relented. Perhaps it was the look of mute appeal on Sandra's face that led her to promise, 'If you still feel you can't go through with it by the time you get back, we'll talk. All I ask you to do now is go and meet Stein, if not for my sake, then his.'

All the way across London in the taxi Sandra wondered why she had spinelessly agreed to Alexandra's demands. The fault must lie in the fact that although she had more or less run Gran's small household she had had no experience in managing her own life. Gran had been a matriarch in her own right and to the last had liked her own way—certainly in every matter that counted. Long since Sandra had given up any idea of asserting herself as this used to upset the old lady, and she doubted now if she still possessed the ability to speak her mind. For someone of Alexandra's dominating nature she must have proved a walkover.

A deep shiver ran all the way down Sandra's limbs as a few minutes later she pressed the bell of Stein Freeman's flat. If ever she survived this first encounter with him she intended to make it her last—as his fiancée. Somehow, something else must be arranged!

She was so busy with her thoughts that when the door in front of her eventually opened she almost jumped. Before her stood a tall man with a great breadth of shoulder. He was dark, so dark that she was glad she had discovered he had Greek blood in his veins or she might have been even more startled than she was already.

There was an odd silence as he stared at Sandra and she could only think blankly that he looked like any normal person. As he stood there no one would ever guess he couldn't see. She recognised him from his photograph. His face had the exact rugged contours, the same straight nose and deeply cleft chin. It was the hint of arrogance that lifted it out of the ordinary. This, and the cool, direct look from the dark grey eyes. It was scarcely a lover-like glance he bent on Sandra, and again she felt herself quiver.

'Alexandra?' His query betrayed what his eyes had failed to reveal and she felt a renewed surge of pity, a sense of compassion which was immediately replaced by confusion as she wondered if Alexandra usually kissed him. It would seem natural to kiss one's fiancé, but it was one of the more obvious points Alexandra and she had never thought of, although Alexandra had said Stein wasn't demonstrative.

'Yes!' she replied quickly, trying to pull herself together as he repeated her name again, this time with a small hint of impatience. Then, marvelling at her own audacity, she brushed past him into the hall. 'You were expecting me?'

'I wasn't sure,' he said sardonically, closing the door and following her as she crossed to the sitting room, moving decisively as she guessed Alexandra would, 'seeing that you haven't been here for three days.'

'But . . .' Sandra's voice trailed off uncomfortably as her eyes widened. If Alexandra hadn't been here last night then where had she been?

'Don't worry,' Stein drawled, coming close to her, his hands reaching out to take her coat, 'I know you have to work. That's why I didn't ring you. Where did your last assignment take you?'

'Oh—er—Brighton,' Sandra gasped, hoping he would put down her shortage of breath to the struggle she was having in getting rid of her coat. What on earth was her cousin playing at? Brighton was the first place to enter her head.

'Poor Alexandra! You're a devil for punishment. Brighton at this time of year! What was Carl thinking about?'

This was getting worse, especially as Stein sounded so cynical. She had heard of Carl Lennox, of course, Alexandra's favourite photographer, but she knew practically nothing about him. From the sound of Stein, he knew plenty! Irrationally Sandra did the first thing she thought of. She slipped her hand through Stein's arm and pulled him gently towards the settee. 'Come and sit down, darling,' she begged softly. 'I'm sure we don't want to discuss Carl.'

'Which makes a change!' Stein's eyebrows rose sarcastically, but he didn't seem to mind sitting beside her.

As she withdrew her hand from his arm he said, 'I presume there's something more important?'

Sandra flushed and was glad he couldn't see it. She felt stunned that she had been able to speak at all naturally, but she doubted if she could continue to do so. Stein Freeman was much more intimidating than she had imagined he would be, there was a hardness about him which made her shrink, but he also made her feel terribly vulnerable. She had felt sorry for him even before she had seen him, but to be near him stirred her heart with a frightening anguish that such a man could be so disabled. 'There's nothing I want to talk about particularly,' she said, feeling choked.

Indifferently he stretched his long, powerful legs, his mouth curling to a sneer. 'It sounds as though I'm in for an entertaining evening. As usual you don't ask how I am.'

'I'm sorry,' anxiously Sandra tried to emulate her cousin's cool tones. 'How are you, Stein?'

'Quite well,' he returned the coolness. 'But a little warmth, a little more enthusiasm, wouldn't come amiss.'

Sandra's thick lashes flickered. What exactly did he mean by that? She suspected he wasn't in the least interested in his own health and there was a devilish glint of irony in his eyes which had her uneasy. It seemed the doctor had been right in thinking his nerves weren't too good, but she didn't want to be on the receiving end of his bad temper. Blinking again, she tried to remember. Hadn't the doctor advised patience?

Yet the situation was so strange, and she felt so apprehensive, she found herself mumbling inanely, 'You'll probably feel better after you've had something to eat.'

His snort of laughter proclaimed that he wasn't impressed either. 'Still the greedy little paragon, Alexandra! You always did believe food the cure for everything, and you so thin.'

Glancing at him quickly, Sandra wondered what reply she could make to this. Her first effort seemed to have sapped what little confidence she had. Now she couldn't think of anything to say which wouldn't seem stilted. 'I don't think you would care for me if I were fat,' she said at last, beating back a half hysterical desire to giggle at her own originality.

'How do you know I wouldn't?' he asked, his hand reaching out suddenly and taking hers as it lay on her lap, as if he knew exactly where to find it. 'Dear me,' he grinned, without much mirth, 'why the clenched fingers? It's most unlike you, my darling, to let me disturb you.'

In vain Sandra tried to free herself, feeling a strange flicker of something like fire going right through her, choosing to end in the most sensitive regions of her body. She had felt it before, as she had innocently drawn Stein towards the settee, and put it down to imagination. But this tremor was too strong to be explained away as a coincidence.

'You don't disturb me,' she protested, perhaps unwisely, as she belatedly remembered the first thing Alexandra would have demanded. 'I think I would like a drink.'

His mouth derisive, he almost threw her hand back to her side. Gratefully she decided he hadn't noticed how she trembled. After all, she was supposed to be his fiancée, and if he felt her reacting nervously he might take it into his devious head to discover why. It was no use Alexandra declaring she and Stein were not compatible. He might still feel he had some rights, especially as she still wore his ring, and, in spite of everything, he was still supposed to be in love with her. Yet his attitude this evening had been far from loving. As she watched him rise and go to the drinks cabinet, Sandra's gaze followed him, full of confusion.

'Food and drink never interest me nowadays,' Stein quipped dryly, pouring two double whiskys. 'I find myself wondering if I shouldn't try to be a more satisfactory lover. We've never really tried very hard in that direction. We might have more to offer each other than we think.'

# CHAPTER TWO

SANDRA seemed to feel every nerve in her body tighten as Stein spoke. As she reached out automatically to accept the drink he offered her mind whirled in such fright she forgot it was whisky, something she wasn't used to having. In her grandmother's house, in the latter years anyway, there had only been the occasional bottle of sherry, and even when out with friends Sandra had rarely indulged in anything stronger.

Trying despairingly to base her reply on a rather vague recollection of what Alexandra had told her, she tried to speak evenly above her unsteady pulse. 'You've never wanted to be my lover yet, so why should you change your mind now?'

He smiled sardonically as he turned without error to press a bell in the wall. 'I'm not sure,' he confessed brutally, 'unless it's boredom which makes me seek a possible way to alleviate it. You're very desirable, my dear, but I don't forget you've never been a particular advocate of sex before marriage.' He paused, a slight frown creasing his broad brow as he turned again in her direction before continuing with a frankness that shook her, 'Do I detect something which seems to indicate that you might feel differently about going to bed with a man? I've never asked you before, Alexandra, but tonight your voice seems softer, rounder somehow, to hold more promise.'

'Please stop!' Sandra's entreaty was barely more than a horrified whisper. Any relief that Alexandra must have indeed been speaking the truth regarding her exact relationship with Stein was lost in a flood of embarrassment. No man had ever spoken to her like this before and the heat in

23

her cheeks seemed to be flooding her very body. Yet she must try to remember that, in the circles Stein and Alexandra moved in, such a conversation might be commonplace. 'Nothing has altered,' she managed to gasp, fearful that Stein might mistake her quivering silence for surrender.

'So,' he shrugged dryly, 'my developing sensitivity isn't as infallible as I thought. Or is it just my present affliction which makes you shudder with distaste?'

Shaken, Sandra flinched from his hardening tones, wondering however she was going to extricate herself from a situation that was becoming more dangerously disquieting by the minute. While she had been attracted by Stein's photograph this hadn't prepared her for the strength of emotion that seemed to hit her as she stared at him now. She wasn't sure what it was—it might merely be pity, but it left her weak and trembling, her only desire to comfort him. There was in her a frightening inclination to put her arms around him, to allow him to do as he wished with her, to reassure him fervently that he was still a man any woman might want, despite his blindness. It seemed intolerable, to her young, feverish way of thinking, that Alexandra had chosen to leave him, especially in this way.

Sandra sighed, more deeply than she knew, as she tried to put her anger aside and answer as she imagined Alexandra might. 'Your present affliction has nothing to do with my feelings in that direction, Stein, as you must know. I can't understand why you keep on about it!'

His face changed to a wry but not desperate resignation. 'I'm sorry, Alexandra, I didn't mean to tease. Greeson was here this afternoon and he always puts me in a black mood, but I don't have to take it out on you.'

Sandra, who had no idea who Greeson was, sought to distract Stein before he could say more about him. 'I know how you feel,' she said quickly. 'You don't have to apologise. Why not have your drink and relax?'

'Cheers,' he quipped tonelessly, lifting his glass, draining half of it in one go as a knock came on the door.

Breathing a sigh of relief, she watched as he let a waiter in with their dinner and, while his back was turned, she tipped the contents of her own glass into a nearby rose bowl. With a rueful grimace she hoped the roses would appreciate it more than she had done!

Over dinner, which Stein handled so expertly she was again hard put to it to believe he couldn't see, she accepted a little red wine with her steak, but only one glass. When Stein insisted she have more she refused, protesting unthinkingly that she wasn't used to it.

She wasn't aware of the mistake she had made until he laughed sarcastically, 'I've never asked you to give up your bad habits, my dear, just because we're going to Greece.'

Greece! She watched the harsh light from the centre fitment play over his dark face and the thought of being with him on a pagan island made her shudder even more than her immediate gaffe over the wine. She had forgotten Alexandra was so fond of it. 'Greece,' she repeated aloud, as the waiter brought their coffee and then silently departed. 'Are you sure,' she entreated cravenly, 'you still want me to accompany you?'

'I haven't any other guide dog,' he retorted grimly, his grey eyes uncannily accurate on hers, so that she felt exposed to some suddenly scornful disapproval within them. 'Besides,' he taunted, 'aren't you coming to find out if you really love me?'

'Of course,' she muttered, feeling as helpless as though she were lost at sea in a small boat. Not even the waves might have made her feel as sick as she did now. Quickly, knowing she must change the subject or confess everything, she left her own chair, going around to his. 'Come and have coffee,' she tried to infuse a coaxing note through her tight throat. Her hand lifted, not quite touching his arm. 'Can't I help you?'

'For God's sake, Alex,' he snarled, immediately informing her she had done the wrong thing, 'you know I can manage in here. I should be an imbecile if I couldn't, after the practice I get.'

Moving away from him as if stung, she retreated to the settee, clenching her fingers around the coffee pot which the waiter had placed on a low table before it and trying frantically to stop herself from shaking. Stein's nerves must be taut if he could speak like this to someone he was supposed to love. Sandra felt her own might soon be as bad if she didn't get away from him. Perhaps in a few minutes she might make some excuse and go?

Steadying her voice wasn't easy, but eventually she managed, 'I'm sorry.' She poured his coffee, adding sugar and milk, passing it to him as he followed silently and sat down by her side. She was conscious of his dark strength, the muscled hardness of his thigh and above all the strange flicker of remembered fire in her body as her hand touched his.

'Don't tell me you're getting sensitive, my darling,' he jeered.

Not sure what he was referring to, she uttered the first thing to enter her head. 'Do you get—I mean, have you had many visitors?'

'Enough.' His pause was significant. 'I've had half a dozen today, all full of good intentions and curiosity. Still, it does pass the time until I get down to working again. How's the typing going? Have you been practising?'

'Practising?' The blank state of Sandra's mind caused her to blink with dismay. 'Oh, yes!' As she dazedly recalled what Alexandra had told her, her exclamation was too quick. 'At least,' she indulged in a glorious rashness, 'it will be something to pass the time in—Greece.'

'There could be other diversions.'

'What—such as?' she asked blankly, while wishing fervently that she didn't have to study her every question and answer with such totally unnatural hesitation. How soon, she wondered, before he noticed?

His narrowed glance was swiftly speculative and taunt-ing. 'Oh, the usual sort,' he drawled, taking a slow sip of his coffee before setting it down again. 'A little wandering and romanticism in the moonlight. Greek moonlight can be extremely potent, Alexandra, even for those usually in control of their emotions. Doesn't the thought of your pos-sible seduction excite you a little?'

'No, definitely not!' Feverishly Sandra dug her nails into her palms, again glad he couldn't see the startled flush on her face. Maybe Alexandra had been right to desert this man with his sensuous look of a prowling tiger! With a strangely intensified awareness she wondered what a girl would be like after spending weeks on a lonely Greek island with a man such as this. Her eyes went over him reluctantly as she sat beside him. He had taken off his jacket and loosened his tie. Beneath the open top button of his shirt, at the base of his strong neck, lay a mat of thick dark hair proclaiming an exciting but dangerous mascu-linity. Quickly she averted her wandering gaze, but not before she had found time to be curious about the number of women he had had affairs with. 'I think,' she choked, 'I'll find greater satisfaction in work. And you did promise ...'

What exactly he had promised she wasn't really sure. Alexandra had only mentioned it vaguely. It might be wiser to leave now and see Alexandra, to have a few things more clearly defined!

But as she made to jump to her feet, as if guessing her intention, his hand shot out and caught her. 'I never pro-mised not to kiss you, did I Alexandra? It's something we've both neglected, but tonight I seem to have an odd fancy.'

As his voice faded he suddenly jerked her against him and, before she could find the breath to protest, his hand raked the back of her head and his mouth found hers.

It was what Sandra had been least expecting. Or expect-ing most—she wasn't sure, but the moment his lips touched hers she knew it for a disaster. A disaster for her as a flame leaped between them, something instantaneous and immediately searing. Around her his firm hands were suddenly rough, slipping down her back to her narrow waist, then up higher, cupping her breasts until she was shivering. She was aware of his mouth, his lips, after their first assault, moving sensitively, trying to force hers apart, and terror of the ultimate outcome, should she surrender to this flood-tide of feeling, gave her the strength to draw back. Everything within her protested that she was in danger of learning too much too swiftly, that Stein Freeman was never a man to allow her one step at a time when he was also moved with primitive desire. Horrified, she pushed him feverishly away.

For a long time he remained completely still, to her relief not attempting to detain her as a slow frown gathered on his forehead. Then, when he seemed about to grasp her again, she started away from him. 'I must go, Stein,' she cried, reaction setting in so rapidly she knew that if she didn't she might easily burst into tears. Either this or start begging him to kiss her again, and she didn't know which would be worst! She was aware of the craziness of a situation that made it impossible for her to tell him exactly what she thought of him for kissing her the way he had. After all, she was supposed to be his fiancée! The sooner she saw Alexandra and told her the whole thing was impossible, the better she would like it.

As she paused in utter mortification, Stein seemed to hesitate before nodding surprisingly. 'If you must,' he agreed suavely. 'Perhaps we both have something to think over.'

'Yes.' She was so busy scrambling quickly into her coat she didn't hear his voice deepen in contemplation. 'Take care of yourself,' she added breathlessly, belatedly thinking there must have been something more she could have done for him than share his dinner and pour coffee. He must be extremely helpless here on his own, in spite of his determined independence. No wonder he wanted to be in Greece among his relations. 'Stein?' she asked, an unconscious note of pleading in her voice. 'Isn't there anything I can do for you?'

'A lot,' he murmured, following her to the door, 'but for the meantime it might be sufficient if you promise to return tomorrow. I don't wish to wait another three days and there are still a few things to discuss before we leave for Greece.'

'Greece?' she stuttered, as though she'd never heard of such a place.

'Yes, Greece,' he taunted. 'You haven't forgotten we fly there on Friday, Alexandra? What's the matter, my dear?' he added, when she made no reply. 'Are you frightened that alone with me on Kalnos you won't be able to control that surprising bit of lasciviousness which almost betrayed you when I kissed you just now?'

Sandra could have told him she felt frozen with fright just standing here—fright, and another emotion she could put no name to. 'How dare you talk to me like that!' she gasped. 'You make me sound positively indecent!'

'Another few minutes on my settee,' he jeered, 'and I could almost guarantee you'd have been acting that way.' His hand streaked out to grasp her wrist, as instinctively he sensed her retreat. 'Why have you always kept your emotions so well hidden until now?'

'I don't know what you're talking about!' She was so confused she scarcely noticed he held her. She didn't know what to expect. Further insults, perhaps, or another assault of some kind? Whatever the cause she felt herself trembling. Yet all he did was drop her arm, so suddenly she felt startled.

'Forget it,' he rejoined curtly. 'I may not find it worth the effort to delve under the ice. A man could drown in such a situation, while leaving the ice relatively unscathed.'

Illusions, my dear, tend to plague a man who can't see. His senses are inclined to exaggerate everything. He's inclined to get excited over what's only a trick of the imagination. You can rest assured, my frigid Alexandra, that your virginity, should you still have it, is quite safe with me.'

'Stein!'

'I'd advise you to just shut up and go,' he drawled, a thin smile lending a cool indifference to his words. 'As I mentioned before, I'll see you tomorrow. That much you can remember.'

On the way back to Alexandra's flat Sandra decided firmly that she wasn't going through with it. Earlier she had been partly resigned, convinced she would be extremely foolish to turn such an opportunity down. Five thousand pounds, when she had had time to think it over, had seemed like a fortune, an answer to all her problems and prayers, but now that she had actually met Stein Freeman she was realising fast just how utterly gullible she had been. That the scheme Alexandra had hatched up had even began to appeal to Sandra's young thirst for adventure seemed now incredible. How had either of them supposed she would be able to go through with it, that she might have the intelligence or ability to continue to deceive a man like Stein Freeman?

Yet not even to herself would Sandra confess she hadn't found it so completely impossible until he kissed her. Furtively, as if there was someone to see, she licked her tongue around dry lips. He had, she supposed, only kissed her lightly, and, while she had been half expecting that he might want to kiss his fiancée, Sandra had been totally unprepared for the response he had aroused within her. She had wanted to melt against him, wanted his mouth to linger, their kiss to deepen, even when her untried emotions had grown alarmed. She would never confess it, but the hint of sensuality he talked of had flared within her, something so new and strange as to be suddenly terrifying, her one defence seeming to be to fight it although every instinct had pleaded otherwise.

What, she wondered unhappily, had his exact relationship been with Alexandra? Alex had sworn she had never had an affair with him, but she had once hinted that, having Greek blood in his veins, he was not reputed to be a cold man. How then had she kept him at a distance? Far from him being cold, Sandra sensed that under his somewhat grim exterior lay a darkly passionate nature. No girl might escape him if he really decided he wanted her, but what the outcome of such an affair might be Sandra had neither the experience or desire to conjecture.

Paying off the taxi took only seconds. With her mind concentrated solely on Stein Freeman, she pressed more than was necessary into the man's hand and was rewarded with an appreciative grin. Grateful for the first sign of warmth she seemed to have found in London yet, Sandra smiled back faintly as he drove away.

But her smile faded rapidly as she hurried into the high building where her cousin lived. That man could see, he wasn't blind. He wasn't a man who could be deceived, the way she and Alexandra were planning to deceive Stein! Numbly Sandra was glad she had come to her senses in time. Alexandra must be made to acknowledge her responsibilities. It was quite obvious that Stein wasn't yet up to facing the unhappiness of a broken engagement, so Alexandra must agree to go with him to his Greek island. That the thought of Alexandra in Greece with Stein seemed to hurt beyond everything else was something Sandra knew she must endeavour to ignore.

Another shock awaited her, however, after she let herself into the flat with her spare key. Alexandra wasn't there. There was only a note, lying on the small hall table, explaining that she had gone.

'By the time you get this,' the hastily written scrawl went, 'I shall be well on my way. I won't say where, but I'll tell you Arnold and I expect to be married tomorrow, so there's nothing you can do about it now. I'm sorry for the hasty departure, but I dared not risk being here when you returned, as I have a great suspicion you might have changed your mind. You always were a timid little mouse, otherwise you'd never have stayed so long with Gran. Now I suggest you'll have to stiffen that upper lip and stick it out. Unless you want a tragedy on your conscience?'

Alexandra added a P.S. 'Arnold has arranged for you to have the agreed five thousand pounds. If you contact his solicitor at the enclosed address he has all the details. You never know, my dear, play your cards right and Stein might be even more generous.'

Feeling numb with shock, Sandra stared at the sheet of paper in her hands. Overcome, she was stunned by a terrible despair, wondering just what she had let herself in for. Alexandra had obviously been crafty enough to sum the situation up. She had even, by veiled insults, managed to imply that she was acting as much for Sandra's good as her own. Her last sentence didn't bear thinking about. Sandra even felt ashamed, at that moment, that she had such a cousin. As for the money, she resolved she would never touch it.

It was some time later before she was able to pull herself together sufficiently to drag herself to the kitchenette to make a cup of tea. There was a horrible taste in her mouth and she felt quite sick. Carefully she wiped a trickle of perspiration from her brow, pushing back the heavy hair from off her small ears in an effort to obtain some coolness. She felt trapped in a welter of fear and disillusion, not remembering, even when Gran had been so ill at the end, ever feeling like this.

Her first reaction, when she felt a little calmer, was to go straight back to Stein and confess everything. She had, in fact, switched off the kettle again and reached the outer door before she realised the terrible position in which

Alexandra had placed her. Her legs almost giving way beneath her, she shrank down on the hall chair. As Alexandra had so vindictively pointed out, how could she live afterwards, if Stein did anything fatal, with such a thing on her conscience? Alexandra's conscience, Sandra decided bitterly, didn't appear to trouble her at all.

All through the night Sandra was unable to sleep as surges of indecision and terror shook her, yet by morning she felt strangely calm. Any possibility of telling Stein the truth seemed to have gone, for to do this might almost amount to murder. How must it feel to be blinded then deserted by someone one loved? To deal out another blow, even if she could bring herself to do it, was, Sandra knew, beyond her. Somehow she must, as Alexandra advised, stick it out. Then, perhaps after they had been in Greece a little while, after the herb-laden breezes, the peace and the sunshine had worked their own healing, she might tell him. There she would find a way of doing it gently, so that the hurt wouldn't be so drastic, and shock, if any, would perhaps be alleviated by the presence of his no doubt adoring grandmother. It was reassuring, if anything could be, to know that so far he suspected nothing. He had accepted her without question as Alexandra. All she must do now was continue the charade with as much confidence as possible—and, she added despairingly, without worrying too much about what to do if Stein tried to kiss her again.

In spite of her having spent the whole day assuring herself nothing could go wrong, it was with marked apprehension that Sandra prepared to visit Stein again that evening. It seemed ridiculous to wear a pretty dress, to take such special care with her face and make-up when he wasn't able to see her. She didn't want to admit, each time she recombed her hair and renewed her lipstick, that it was merely to put off the moment when she could no longer delay her departure.

Stein was waiting for her as she had known he would

be. On her way to the flat she had been unconsciously pray-
ing he might have been called away, but unfortunately this
was not to be. He was there, opening the door moments
after she rang, courteously guiding her to the lounge after
removing her wrap, as though she was the one without
sight. She could feel his absolute control of the situation,
sense his dominant personality. Maybe, Sandra thought,
staring at him nervously, both she and Alexandra might
have been wrong in thinking him vulnerable. He was so
decisive, giving such an impression of rugged strength
that she was the one to feel weak and exposed.

'You're a little late.' He went over, after seeing her
seated, and began sorting through bottles. 'I got it into my
head you weren't coming, but you wouldn't let me down,
would you, my darling?'

'Why—no,' Sandra faltered, torn between the note of
sarcasm in his voice and what he was doing. He was filling
two glasses. Could she continue feeding his roses with
whisky. Mightn't it be more sensible to pretend she had
changed her drinking habits? 'Would you mind, Stein,'
she begged, before giving herself time to fully consider, 'if
I had something soft to drink? I seem to have had an awful
day.'

'A soft drink?' The way his eyebrows rose might have
warned her. 'Just what did you have in mind, Alexandra?
I can't remember hearing you ask for such a thing before.'

'Oh, anything,' she tried desperately to adopt Alexandra's
careless indifference. 'Soda and a splash of lime, I'm not
fussy. Just anything you have.' As her voice trailed away
she began to wish she had never asked. There was a
sardonic smile on his lips which made her uneasy.

She watched, astonished that he spilled nothing, as his
hands moved deftly, half filling a glass from the soda siphon
before topping it up with something else. 'I think this will
be to your liking,' he told her suavely.

Rather than fidget where she was on her low seat, Sandra

rose to take it from him. 'Drink it up,' he ordered, as she thanked him.

'How are you?' she asked awkwardly, staring unsuspectingly down at the frothy white bubbles before raising the glass to her lips.

One second she was quite all right, the next she was choking. Quickly, alarm jumping through her, she groped for her handkerchief. Whatever he'd put in the glass made her throat tighten and sting like mad. Unable to find her own handkerchief, she grasped the one he held out, rubbing furiously at the tears which came to her eyes.

'Better?' he enquired smoothly a minute later as the spasms stopped.

'What on earth did you put in it?' Her voice was hoarse with indignation and for a moment she forgot to do anything but act naturally.

'Nothing to what I might wish I had put in it, after you've answered a few questions!'

The soft menace in his tones struck Sandra to a horrified silence and he must have heard her sharply drawn breath.

'Surprised?' he jeered. 'The Alexandra I know would have downed that without turning a hair, yet one sip and you splutter and cough like a two-year-old. Not even my roses made such a fuss.'

Half petrified, Sandra tried to calm herself, to laugh coolly as if it were all a joke, but even her voice seemed to be lost. How much had he guessed if he knew about that?

'I wasn't feeling too good last night either,' she managed at last. 'That's why I tipped my drink into the rose bowl.' She knew she should perhaps have challenged him about being so horribly suspicious, but somehow she hadn't the nerve.

He had gone pale, and with a sinking heart she felt his anger as his hands snaked out to take hold of her shoulders, his grip fierce, as if determined she shouldn't escape. 'I

don't know,' he ground out, 'if this is supposed to be a
practical joke, but if it is it's not one I appreciate. Just who
the hell are you? You aren't Alexandra, so don't give me
that!'

More frightened than she could ever recall being in her
life, Sandra almost collapsed under his cruel hands. His
face was tight and hard, his eyes focussing squarely on her,
giving the impression that he could see with icy clearness.
While she knew he couldn't she was also aware she could
no more deny the charge he laid against her than she could
go on living a lie.

'How did you guess?' she whispered hoarsely.

His laughter was cynical, expressing his scorn. There was
no amusement in it. 'You betrayed yourself in several ways,'
he assured her, 'although it was some time before anything
really registered. Your refusal to have more than one glass
of wine surprised me. Alexandra, you see, no matter how
tired she was, could always drain the bottle. Then your
mistake with my coffee. She knows only too well I take no
milk or sugar, and you added both. Afterwards I wondered
why the scent of the roses someone was kind enough to
bring me should remind me faintly of whisky. It wasn't
until I dipped my finger in the water that I realised. Want
me to go on?' he asked, overlaying her strangled gasp with
cold fury. 'Shall I tell you what proved conclusive evidence,
after you'd gone and I went over the surprising events of
the evening?'

'What?'

'What!' his sarcasm lashed her harshly as he jerked her
closer to his strong body. 'It seems you're too dumb to
make a good conspirator. Shall I demonstrate how I knew?'
Before she could evade him his head bent and his mouth
came down with force on to hers. Then, as he crushed her
to him, one of his hands slid aggressively over her.

He lifted his head to say viciously, 'The girl I'm engaged
to doesn't have curves like this—and this! Haven't I seen

enough of Alexandra to be familiar with every straight line of her figure? Yours is much more seductive, my dear. Didn't you imagine I would know the difference? There are some things a man doesn't need eyesight to judge. He usually learns of these things in the dark anyway.'

Against his brutality she seemed to have no defence. Insistently his hands increased their pressure until she cried out. He couldn't see the fright on her face, so he had to hear it, she realised, shrinking from his grim satisfaction. She was too bewildered to respond to the shiver of excitement that flicked through her taut nerves, or the way in which her body curved unconsciously to his.

'Yes,' he sneered, his face black, 'protest as much as you like, my little cheat. There's no one to hear you. No one comes here unless I ring.'

'Please let me go,' she begged desperately, trying to break free.

'Why should I?' His hand left her breast to lace through her hair, tugging her head back to his shoulder. 'Why shouldn't you be prepared to pay for your sins? Deceiving a blind man surely couldn't be classed as anything else? Wouldn't you care to brighten his darkness a little by agreeing to spend a few hours in his bed? I can promise you might even enjoy it.'

'No!' she cried wildly, her whole body suffused in a peculiar heat.

'No?' His mouth found the racing pulse in her throat, moving over her tender skin while he appeared to enjoy assessing the exact degree of her terror. From the tenseness of his lean, hard body, she gathered the shaken impression that he would like to have done more than merely assault her with his lips, and when he spoke it seemed with the deliberate intent of insulting her. 'If you won't willingly grant me more than a few lukewarm kisses, girl, then at least I'll have the truth. I warn you I can hurt worse than this. Now tell me—who are you?'

'Sandra Weir ...'

'Sandra Weir?' his voice rasped with impatience. 'Listen, girl, I've heard small boys shouting "pull the other one", but I'm in no mood to appreciate your perverted sense of humour. This is something, I presume, which you and Alexandra hatched up between you. Now, your real name?'

'But I am called Alexandra Weir!' Suddenly almost beside herself with regret, she had no desire to go on evading the answers he so ruthlessly sought, although even the thought of confessing many of the things he would have to know filled her with both alarm and remorse. That the truth was obviously going to hurt him seemed to cause her actual pain and she was glad he couldn't see the tears which sprang unhappily to her green eyes. 'I'm Alexandra's cousin,' she continued hastily, before he could rip into her again. 'I was christened Alexandra, too, for—for family reasons, but because I'm the younger, I've always been known as Sandra.'

'Indeed!' His curt exclamation held sarcastic incredulity and he still retained his tight grip of her shoulders, as if determined she shouldn't escape before he uncovered the whole diabolical truth. 'And was this little charade arranged for any particular reason? I presume Alexandra is away on an assignment about which she preferred not to tell me? Why, in heaven's name, didn't she just explain frankly?' His strong mouth twisted. 'We surely could have worked something out. I hope I'm not that terrifying, or helpless!'

'No. No, of course not,' Sandra mumbled, trying to think straight. 'There were reasons she didn't want you to know.'

'Reasons?' he grunted ominously. 'There'd better be, although I don't think you'd find one good enough to impress me now. What craziness led Alexandra to go to such ridiculous lengths? I take it she intends to return before Friday?'

Trembling, Sandra stared at him, wishing fervently that she could conveniently faint. What could she tell him that wouldn't seem like striking a man when he was down? Stein spoke quietly but she could feel the leashed anger in him. For this she couldn't blame him, as no one appreciated being made a fool of. She shuddered to envisualise his re- actions when he knew all. If only it were possible to pre- tend Alexandra was only away working—but this, Sandra realised, would merely be postponing that which Stein must know sooner or later. There could be no sense in put- ting it off now. It seemed dreadful that she herself, by agree- ing to Alexandra's stupid scheme, should be responsible for so much heartache. It would be little use telling him that, after their meeting last night, she had changed her mind about everything. He wouldn't believe her. If only she had been fully aware of what she was doing before it had been too late!

'I'm sorry,' she whispered, her heart, which just a few minutes ago had been full of resentment at the way he had kissed her, weeping for him. 'Alexandra isn't coming back, now or ever.'

His voice hardened to steel. 'Would you mind being a little more explicit?'

'I——' Sandra's barely won composure broke, 'I scarcely know where to begin.'

'You'd better sit down,' he said curtly. Almost as if he sensed the whiteness of her face he steered her towards the settee. Seating himself beside her, he added grimly, 'I feel you would like to pass out, but you'd better not! Not until you've answered every one of my questions. So Alexandra decided she didn't want to have anything more to do with me? What then?'

Sandra took a deep breath, striving to keep a grip on her churning emotions. 'Alexandra came to see me,' she blurted out, even now not sure she could relate clearly what had taken place. 'I lived in Cornwall, so I rarely saw her, and knew less about her affairs. I knew, of course, of your engagement.' She paused, unable to mention how she had half fallen in love with his photograph. Anyway, that wasn't relevant. 'Well,' she drew another uneven breath, 'she came to see me and told me about your accident, and the fix she was in.'

Tersely he interrupted, 'You mean she couldn't face the fact that I was blind?'

'No!' Sandra denied quickly, not having the heart to agree that this might have been partly true. He was about to be brutally hurt by other things, there was no reason to add to his misery. 'Someone else wants to marry her too, you see, and she felt the shock of knowing this just now might prove too much for you.'

'Alexandra's ego takes a bit of beating!' His laughter was suddenly cynical, his bitterness pinning Sandra to her seat. 'You don't believe in cushioning your somewhat startling announcements, do you, Miss Weir? Am I to presume, from what you say, that your cousin finds this other man irresistible? That she loves him, and wants to marry him rather than me?'

Trying not to hear the harsh sarcasm in his voice, Sandra answered gently, 'I'm sorry to have to tell you this. Believe me, I didn't want to do it. Alexandra only wished to save you as much pain as possible. This way she thought you'd never need to know she'd left you for another man. Acting on her behalf, when you were stronger, I was simply to tell you I'd changed my mind.'

'While pretending to be Alexandra! God!' his voice lanced into her, 'how on earth did the pair of you expect such a stupid scheme to work? Or did your cousin not care?'

'She hoped it would work,' Sandra protested weakly, not knowing why she should be defending Alexandra, who appeared to have played tricks on them both. Frozen with a terrible despair, she stared anxiously at Stein. 'She was convinced you weren't strong enough to stand such a shock, which seems to prove she must care more than you think.'

# CHAPTER THREE

STEIN FREEMAN shrugged this off with a casual movement of his wide shoulders which refuted any suggestion that he was impressed. 'Was she concerned for me or her own public image, I wonder? A nice little scandal if I were to commit hara-kiri or, in a more ladylike way, did she favour the river? She could be flattering herself. No woman, I assure you, Miss Weir, would drive me to that!'

Impulsively Sandra laid a soothing hand on his arm. 'I understand this other man wouldn't allow her to consider going to Greece with you.'

'Why should a few more weeks have made any difference? If she couldn't trust herself alone with me she can't be very enamoured with her new lover.'

That last bit hurt, strangely enough. Had they really been lovers, Stein and Alexandra? Sandra's heart shook. 'Perhaps,' she exclaimed unwisely, 'she felt she couldn't trust you.'

His mouth twisted wryly, as if he enjoyed a private, though not very amusing joke. 'Perhaps you're right.' He paused cynically. 'Does she intend marrying this other man right away, do you know?'

'Almost.'

'Who is he?' Stein asked curtly, shaking off her hand, as if rejecting her impulsively offered comfort.

'I'm sorry,' she flushed, as her hand fell back to her side, 'I promised not to tell.'

'Indeed?' For a moment, seeing the angry tightening of his mouth, Sandra felt afraid, but he merely shrugged again, contemptuously. 'Keep your worthless little secrets,

41

Miss Weir! It will only be a matter of time before I find out.'

Reduced to a quivering silence, Sandra heard him continue grimly, 'As there seems nothing more to be said of Alexandra, might we go on to your part in all this? You agreed to take her place and come to Greece with me, to deceive me to the bitter end? It must have taken quite a sum of money to persuade you, Miss Weir. Just how big was the bribe?'

'The bribe?' Sandra's eyes widened with apprehension as she stared at him. She had been so agitated all day, so busy trying to reach a logical decision, she had forgotten all about the money. After reading Alexandra's instructions about seeing Arnold's solicitor regarding it, she had vowed never to touch it, but today she hadn't given it another thought. Biting her lip, she felt guilty, now that Stein mentioned it, and didn't know what to say.

'No reply?' Stein taunted, his face hard. 'People are usually willing to do anything for money, aren't they, Sandra? You'd better tell me how much it was.'

'Five thousand,' she confessed, while not having intended giving way to his threatening tones. Despairingly she realised his seeming ability to extract information against her will.

'Five thousand!' His voice grated insultingly as he rose to his feet. 'You could be even worse than your cousin!'

'Stein,' she was up beside him, facing him desperately, though she was well aware he couldn't see her, 'you must believe I wasn't going to take it! I changed my mind about everything last night, after I left here. I was going to tell Alexandra so.'

He paused, a quick frown to his brow. 'The money hasn't been paid over?'

'Yes, in a way, but——'

'Little mercenary!' Without waiting to hear the finish of her faltering explanation, he stretched his hand ruthlessly out to drag her to him. 'You don't have to search for excuses. You stand there and confess shamelessly that you agreed to come to Greece with me, a total stranger, for the sake of a few paltry pounds?'

'It's not paltry!'

'How easily you're impressed. For a few drachma,' he sneered, 'what might I not get you to agree to? Did Alexandra not warn you, Sandra, exactly what you were taking on?'

Trembling in his hands, Sandra tried to remain calm. She hadn't meant to make that comment about the money, making it sound as if she found it irresistible, but for so long she and Gran had scrimped and done without that it seemed sacrilege to pour scorn on a single penny. 'You don't understand,' she replied hollowly. 'I hadn't a job and Alexandra said you really wanted a sort of secretary to help with your work.'

'Fair enough,' he snarled, 'but you can't conveniently forget the other commitment. You agreed to pretend to be my fiancée and it suited you to take what must amount to almost a thousand pounds a week. Don't tell me you didn't realise this must involve more than merely typing a few notes? Didn't Alexandra explain properly?'

'Don't worry.' Sandra's face blanched as her fright and bewilderment grew. It seemed to her Alexandra hadn't explained a lot of things, not clearly. Painfully she swallowed as she tried to apologise to the man who bent so angrily over her. 'You can forget about the money, it's not important. I'm sorry for all the trouble I've caused, but I promise I won't bother you again. As I've already said, I was going to tell Alexandra last night that I couldn't do it, but when I returned to her flat she'd already gone.'

'You expect me to believe that?'

'You probably won't.' Helplessly she shrugged under his biting fingers. 'I don't think you would be inclined to believe anything good of me at the moment.'

'I've had little cause to.'

'I suppose not.' Suddenly she found herself examining his face closely, her resentment superseded by a growing anxiety. He must have been very ill and Alexandra had emphasised that he couldn't stand another shock. While Stein's splendid physique seemed to deny this she could see plainly the lines of strain around his eyes and mouth. Alexandra's behaviour must be hurting him terribly. Under that inscrutable front he could be suffering like the devil. 'I really am sorry about Alexandra,' she whispered, 'and I'm beginning to realise just how you must feel. You must want to be alone, so I'll go now. Anyway, there's no point in my staying any longer.'

'Oh no, you don't!' His voice was so harshly determined that she shrank. 'This despicable scheme which you and Alexandra devised between you could only have worked if you were able to type.'

'I can,' Sandra admitted reluctantly. 'I worked for a writer for a few months, but he was nothing like you. I couldn't work for you!'

'Why couldn't you?' he asked coldly. 'Since my eyes stopped helping me think, my brain has been forced to work twice as hard. Did you imagine I would let you escape so easily, so that you might share your little joke with your friends? You can consider you've been trapped by your own greed, Sandra Weir, and there's no way you can avoid the consequences of your own folly! You'd better be prepared to start earning that five thousand, for by heavens I'll see that you sweat for every penny—in more ways than one!'

Sandra, feeling her body go stiff with returning apprehension, protested faintly, 'But I've already told you I'm not taking any money!'

'That's up to you,' he sneered, 'but whether you do or not, you're coming with me! I'm leaving on Friday. Even if I wished there's no time to find anyone else. Also, you will come as my fiancée. As Alexandra craftily realised, your names being basically the same makes such a proposition almost foolproof. For the few days, during which we'll visit my grandmother, I'll have enough pity to endure without inviting more by turning up without you.'

'Please,' Sandra begged, the strain in her voice clearly audible, 'I know how ill you must have been, but this doesn't give you the right to talk to me like this. I won't do what you ask, and you can't make me!'

'I can and I will!' The hardness of his tones betrayed no sign of weakening. 'How old are you, Sandra? You're younger than your cousin, but I want to know by how much.'

'I'm twenty-one,' she gasped, trying to gather her wits to form some decisive argument against him.

'Ah!' His hands left her narrow shoulders to cradle her face and, momentarily, his voice seemed softer. 'Already I'd guessed, almost exactly from the slender contours of your body, but I have yet to see your face. I'm sorry, but this is the only way I can do it,' he said mockingly, his fingers lingering over each separate feature. 'A neat nose, slightly tilted, which speaks of some spirit,' he drawled sardonically as his hands traced her. 'Eyes well spaced and brows winged, if I'm not mistaken. Skin like silk'— his hand moved tentatively along the clear, tender line of her jaw, 'and a mouth I'm already sufficiently familiar with to want to know better. There's a warmth about you, my child, that I never found in Alexandra.'

'Perhaps you didn't search hard enough?' Wildly Sandra jerked away from him, her cheeks scarlet, her heart pounding nervously.

'Unfortunately it's now too late,' he retorted dryly. 'She's gone to a higher bidder.'

'How do you know that?' Sandra whispered, horrified.

Suddenly, as if she no longer interested him, he let her go. 'Didn't he pay out five thousand for her?' he asked, insultingly. 'Men who part with that kind of money are not usually paupers.'

Sandra's heart ached as she realised how Stein must be suffering. 'She might come back.'

'It has been known,' he returned enigmatically, 'but that remains to be seen.'

Did this mean he would welcome her? Mysteriously disconcerted, Sandra turned, groping for her wrap with numb fingers. There seemed nothing more to say.

'You may go now,' he muttered magnanimously, with his uncanny perception of her every movement, 'but you'd better return in the morning! I must assure myself that you're familiar with all the arrangements for our departure on Friday. There are also several things still to see to.'

'And if I refuse?' she challenged, while aware with a fatalistic feeling of defeat that she dared not.

She couldn't tell if he sensed her ultimate surrender, she only heard the implacable ring to his parting words.

'Whether you do or not is entirely up to you, but if you don't I'll see that you suffer! Not only you but Alexandra, too. You will find, my dear, that a blind man is just as capable of revenge as one who has unimpaired vision.'

Sandra, who had never been abroad before, found the journey almost unbearably exciting, in spite of the tension still within her regarding her uneasy relationship with Stein. As she sat on the huge plane beside him, before they landed at Athens airport, she found herself nervously twisting the engagement ring she wore until it made a red mark on her finger.

Almost as if he could actually see what she was doing, Stein moved his hand sideways to cover her own. 'We'll soon be down,' he said quietly. 'There's nothing to worry about, although I realise this is your first flight.'

To hide her nervousness Sandra stared broodingly at their entwined hands. To the casual onlooker they must appear like absorbed lovers, but she knew this was far from the case. Stein, behind the dark glasses which he usually scorned, appeared so strong and full of masculine vitality that he attracted a great deal of feminine attention, while Sandra, being by contrast slender and fair, had been surveyed contemplatively from several pairs of masculine eyes. None of this really bothered her, but Stein's hand over her own did. Yet she made no obvious effort to remove it, too aware of his terse impatience which seemed ever ready to scorch her most innocent action or remark.

To avoid this as much as possible she had found herself agreeing to most things he had asked of her during the last few days, but she had rebelled against wearing Alexandra's ring. Pocketing her pride, she almost begged to be allowed to use, instead, a small eternity ring, one which her grandmother had given her on her last birthday, It wasn't expensive, but somehow it seemed much more endearing than Alexandra's huge diamond. 'Besides,' she had told Stein, 'it's far too valuable. 'I'd be worrying continually that I might lose it.'

He had slipped the diamond ring into his pocket, as if it was of no consequence, and knowing of her cousin's expensive tastes, Sandra had wondered however Alexandra had managed to part with it. No doubt her new fiancé must have given her something even more expensive. 'You're probably right,' Stein had shrugged. Then, not so carelessly, 'Though when the day does come that I really want to adorn your slender hand with something more valuable you'd better be prepared to accept it.'

Sandra hadn't replied, simply because her pulse had been beating too fast and she couldn't visualise such a time coming. Between them, she acknowledged, was a kind of half-hidden, smouldering attraction but little sympathy. They struck too many sparks off each other. It made for the kind of discord which was far from soothing, especially as she was the one who must always give in! He would, she feared, impose his will entirely over hers if she gave him the chance. It was becoming, she suspected, an amusing game with him to taunt her beyond endurance, and this was one of the reasons why she had agreed to make an immediate start on his new book. It distracted him, giving him something to do other than to pander to the sometimes restless turbulence within him. They had, in fact, almost completed the first chapter which, when she read it back to him, had seemed to prove satisfactory.

'We'll revise it on the island,' he said. 'I think it only needs a few alterations.' His firmly shaped mouth had twisted derisively. 'Do you know I've never worked with anyone like this before. I never really thought I would be able to. I did try with Alexandra——' He had broken off abruptly, as if reluctant to voice the opinion which hovered on his lips. Even so, Sandra had been unable to subdue a small glow of pleasure. Perhaps, if she could derive some satisfaction from helping him, she might forget the resentment she felt in being virtually blackmailed into going to Greece.

She still wondered why she had gone back to the flat as he had commanded. It still remained a mystery why she had presented herself to him so humbly next day and allowed him to treat her like an inferior servant ever since. She shivered, her fingers tightening unconsciously within his large hand as she considered his treatment of her. Occasionally he could be almost civil, willing to talk of ordinary things, like the weather and various items of news from the radio, but mostly he only addressed her with orders to see to this and that. There were jobs, she suspected, which irked him not being able to do himself, yet sometimes she was amazed by the number of things he had obviously taught himself to do. When, now and again, he carried his independence too far she had learnt not to rush immediately to his rescue. For then he would snarl at her or jerk her savagely to him, as if it would give him great pleasure to do her some actual physical injury.

Later he might apologise, but not always, and as it seemed merely lip service when he did she preferred it when he remained darkly uncommunicative. It was as if he imagined, after Alexandra's defection, he owned Sandra body and soul, and she often felt tempted to remind him that Alexandra had only been engaged to him, nothing more binding.

If she had thought the days before their departure to Greece would drag, she need not have worried. Stein kept her extremely busy. While she had impressed on him that she was not a properly trained secretary, he appeared to think she should be capable of almost anything, should she apply herself.

'You're learning,' he had said grimly, as she escorted him halfway across London to see his publisher.

'I think, under the circumstances, he could have come to you,' she had dared point out, her arm conscious of the hard pressure of his fingers. Stein refused to use a white stick, just as he usually declined to wear his dark glasses and, apart from his reliance on her long-suffering arm, managed very well.

'You've nothing else to do,' he had replied curtly. 'And I pay you to help me. As we're supposed to be lovers people don't think anything of us walking arm in arm. It never occurs to them that I have anything wrong with me.'

He hadn't seemed to remember that she was an absolute stranger to London and had no idea where to find many of the places he would suddenly demand to be taken to. Eventually she had given up trying and learnt to rely on the help of kindly taxi drivers. It was when Stein decided they should walk part of the way that she grew confused and had to bear the brunt of his sarcastic comments. Fortunately he could always manage to put her on the right path again, but she resented that he could make her feel so stupid.

The telephone had proved almost more of an ordeal than these somewhat hazardous journeys. Stein, it would seem, had other interests besides writing, and people rang him continually. Sometimes she felt at her wits' end—not knowing what to say to those who wanted to speak to him urgently and whom, Stein assured her, he had no intention of bothering with until he returned from Greece.

'I'll be back soon enough!' Arrogantly he waved aside her indignant reproaches. 'I'll be better able to deal with them then. There's nothing urgent. Don't push me, Sandra.'

As if anyone could do that! 'But they are colleagues,' she had protested, trying to recall even a few of the well-known names she had painstakingly written down.

'Let them wait,' he had grunted indifferently. 'All in good time.'

So she had grown quite clever at devising tactful little excuses, while Stein sat and listened, a sardonic smile on his face. Occasionally it felt more like a year than a week that she had worked for him.

He rarely mentioned Alexandra, although sometimes, when Sandra objected weakly that he treated her like a slave, he would remind her that she was only compensating for her cousin's sins. That she must agree it was poetic justice that she should suffer along with him, and it was only by concentrating on pleasing him that she could hope to redeem herself. All of which proved cold comfort to Sandra, who despaired of his hard words, being already more than a little in love with him.

Athens airport bewildered Sandra by its size and what seemed to her a great deal of noise and confusion.

'Airports are much the same wherever you go,' Stein spoke in her ear cynically. 'The larger they are the worse they seem. You'd better get used to it.'

Again she resented that he made her feel like a child and seemed to enjoy doing so. He made it sound as if she was earmarked for future journeys in his company, and reacting nervously she tugged away from his restraining hand.

'Be still,' he said curtly. 'I'm forced to rely on you, damn you. You can't walk out on me here.'

Shocked by his harsh exclamation, she went rigid, her face white.

Immediately he felt it and must have guessed the reason for her cold tension. 'Forgive me,' he muttered formally, 'but you know I can't manage without you!'

It might have been nice, she thought bitterly, glancing up at his closed face, if that had been uttered with even one twinge of pleading. The way Stein spoke it contained no warmth whatsoever. 'I don't intend you should have to,' she retorted with spirit, 'but sometimes I could discard you happily!'

'Just be thankful we aren't alone,' he sneered, leaving her in little doubt as to his meaning. 'But I have a good memory.'

Wondering miserably what to make of that, she dragged alongside him. He had their passports and, almost as if he could see, he had them quickly through Customs and was speaking to the porter with their luggage. Being able to travel first class had a lot going for it, Sandra decided dryly, as they were bowed into a taxi like royalty.

Stein had said they could have flown straight to Corfu, where his grandmother lived, but he wanted to see a man in Athens, so they drove straight to Syntagma Square where some of the best hotels were to be found. On the way Sandra only had brief glimpses of the city, being relatively surprised when they reached their destination in one piece. The Greeks drove at an amazing and, to her, dangerous speed and didn't seem to know what it was to brake gently. Many times she was literally thrown against Stein, who patiently bore the weight of her startled body twice before advising her that she would be wiser to stay where she was if she wanted to escape undamaged. But to be held close to him like this seemed almost as dangerous, especially when his arm seemed to tighten more than necessary.

The hotel was huge with marble floors, spacious rooms and a restful atmosphere and the manager greeted Stein personally, with an enthusiasm Sandra was beginning to recognise as typically Greek. On their way upstairs Stein mentioned casually that he stayed here quite often, though he just as often stayed with friends.

They were led into a large, self-contained suite of two bedrooms and a lounge, the manager still hovering. Sandra had been surprised by the amount of discussion that had taken place at the desk when they had arrived, but as it had been in Greek, she hadn't understood a word of it.

It was not until the manager was bowing his way out that she was enlightened. 'If this suite is not to your satisfaction, Mr Freeman, you can still have the rooms you initially reserved, or another suite.'

Her cheeks flushing, Sandra waited until the man was finally gone before speaking. 'Why did you change the reservations, Stein? Surely two rooms, side by side, would have been better?'

He simply glanced at her and shrugged, his smile cruel as if he could see her embarrassed face. 'You should be able to dodge a blind man quite easily, *thespinis*,' he used the Greek word for Miss, mockingly. 'I decided this would be more convenient, that's all. Would you have me forever running next door, like a small child, perhaps losing my way?'

She took no notice of his deliberate pathos. 'You know you wouldn't have done that. It seems so ridiculous when you'd already booked.'

'Forget it,' he snapped, as if suddenly impatient and no longer willing to tolerate her complaints. 'That was when I expected your cousin would be with me.'

'Do I not warrant the same—respect?' Sandra asked wildly.

'No,' he replied, then, without further explanation, he turned from her to walk into his own room, adding distinctly before closing the door, 'I will need such assistance as befits a man in my condition, girl, and you'd better be prepared to give it without prattling on about your improbable humiliation.'

Staring at his closed door, Sandra wondered despairingly if there was anything she could do about it. How would he expect her to help him other than in the way she was already doing? While she didn't mind so much running his errands, answering the telephone, doing his typing, anything more personal caused her to tremble. The thought of having to drape a shirt around those broad shoulders, of having to fasten it up against Stein's wide expanse of chest, was more than she dared think about. In how many ways, during the course of such ministrations, might she not betray herself? She could only derive a little comfort from the knowledge that while he often seemed to enjoy deliberately taunting her, he rarely carried out his threats to the letter.

Her bedroom, she found, was comfortable and well furnished, but this scarcely registered as her resentment against Stein refused to be completely mollified. How dared he put her in such a position? Did he expect to come wandering in here while she undressed and bathed, pleading that he couldn't see? Hadn't he told her, on the plane, that his senses were now so acute that they transmitted almost as clear a picture as his eyes had once done. No, she would refuse to have him in here, refuse to do anything more for him at all than she was doing already.

Yet, ten minutes later, she found herself hurrying automatically on hearing him call her name. To her surprise she found him showered and changed in a fresh shirt and light slacks, his thick hair brushed neatly against the strong lines of his well-shaped head. 'How did you manage?' she gasped, aware suddenly that apart from discarding her jacket she had done no more than sit on the edge of her bed.

'I've told you, I've stayed here before,' he replied impatiently, 'and solving the mysteries of one suitcase was comparatively easy. You might have to find a few things for me later, though. Remember I didn't bring my valet.'

'Valet?'

Stein laughed softly. 'You didn't know I had one in London, did you? Actually he just came for an hour, morning and evening, so you never met him.'

'Alexandra never said——'

'Because she never knew about him either,' Stein's voice deepened derisively. 'I don't care that my women should know how helpless I really am.'

'I never thought that!'

'No—but I'm no magician either, Sandra. For some things, such as ensuring I don't wear the same shirts continually, I have to rely on other people.'

'Yes, of course. I do see,' Sandra frowned, wondering just how much more about this man she had yet to find out? 'But here?'

'You will help me, but don't worry,' he relented, a faint smile on his mouth. 'I promise not to ask anything of you that might offend your virginal sense of propriety.'

Her small gasp of indignation must have been a mistake, for swiftly he reached out, drawing her ruthlessly to him, as if using her body to emphasise his next words. 'Not until you're ready,' he mocked.

As she began instinctively to struggle, his arms tightened. 'Stop being so nervous, my dear. I'm not going to assault you.'

'I didn't think you would,' she gulped, 'but why this?'

'You should have more confidence in your own charms,' he grunted. 'Many men would give a lot to have such an innocent young girl in their arms. If that's really what you are?' his lips curled cruelly. 'A blind man would have only one way of finding out.'

'I knew ...' she began, her cheeks flaming.

'You don't,' he stopped her, making no pretence not to understand. He ran one hand over her shoulders without letting her go. 'I'm merely attempting to confirm a suspicion that you haven't done more than sit in your room and shiver since we arrived. Whether in anticipation or apprehension I'm not sure, but there's nothing about you, no dampness to your skin or silky hair, to suggest that you've bathed and changed, as I have.'

'You enjoy mocking me!' she choked, attempting to disguise a sudden shame of her own indolence.

'Perhaps,' he returned enigmatically. 'But this might only be because you appear, so far as I'm concerned, to have developed a habit of suspecting the worst. You are always so terrified, are you not, that I come searching for this?' Without warning, as she trembled, he brought her hard up against him, crushing her shaking lips beneath a mouth which was even more intolerant than his words.

When, moments later, he lifted his head his eyes had darkened perceptibly, and, after a brief hesitation, his mouth moved, with a little more gentleness, over her face while his hand curved her slender nape. His voice thickened slightly as he muttered, 'I believe you have it in you to incite a man to madness.'

'Please let me go,' Sandra begged, wishing feverishly that she could think of something more original, but her head was swimming, her legs curiously weak. The hot surge of feeling which washed through her was caused, she knew, by the disturbing impact of his hard body but, while she wanted only to escape him, she seemed unable to move.

He didn't appear to hear her urgent whisper as his lips discovered the throbbing pulse in her white throat. Helplessly her weighted lashes fell as he cupped her face in his hands and said wryly, 'I regret not being able to look into your eyes, Sandra, to read what lies there. A woman might not always be ready to confess that which a man wishes to hear, but her eyes will often betray her inmost secrets.'

His voice was like a drug, smooth yet insistent, not anything she might effectually fight. 'I'm sure, once you're in Corfu, you'll find someone more interesting to bait, Mr Freeman.'

'Mr Freeman!' As if to punish her for calling him this, his mouth closed over hers again, his arms holding her savagely to him. She tried to resist, but it was like being thrown into the middle of a violent storm, one that surged and ravaged and played havoc with the senses. His mouth and hands, as yet moving with apparent innocence, were arousing in her a degree of response that made her wonder however she would fight him if he really began making love to her. As it was she found it almost impossible to prevent her arm from creeping up to his broad shoulders.

Then, with a strangely unsatisfied sigh, he put her from him. 'Ring for some tea,' he commanded, as if they had merely been discussing the weather. 'We'll have more time for such light dalliance on Corfu. Or should I say, I will. I'll see you have work to keep you occupied, Miss Weir, but no doubt my grandmother, when she sees how you don't really care for me, will find someone more willing to pander, shall we say, to my baser instincts.'

Over tea, for which Sandra found she had little appetite, he told her he had ordered a car and driver to show her a glimpse of the city.

'It's all you'll get, I'm afraid,' he said unrepentantly. 'Later, as you know, I must go out, and I don't want you running around on your own. You might only get lost and appeal to the first man you met, and he might be even more unwilling to stop at a few kisses than I am.'

Her heart faltering, she tried to ignore what he said. 'I'm here to do a job, Stein, I don't have to go out at all. You certainly don't have to take me around like a travel guide. Besides,' she added unthinkingly, 'you can't ...'

'See,' he supplied softly, as she halted aghast. To her relief and embarrassment he didn't seem unduly perturbed by her clumsy blunder. There was even a faint twist of amusement to his strong mouth, as if he enjoyed her confusion. 'I know I can't see, Sandra, but Greece, to me, has always essentially been a land of smells—hot herb smells, flowers, eucalyptus and pine trees. They remind me easily of olives glittering in the sun, burnt grass, hot sands and parched hills. Greece often smells like you, very young, sweet and clean, but perhaps, again like you, she also seems tainted occasionally by that which is less wholesome.'

'You talk as though I were evil!'

'Have you not in your veins the same blood as your cousin?'

How Greek he seemed when he spoke like that! 'Why did you have anything to do with me if I'm so repulsive?'

'I didn't say repulsive, girl. A man can feel beauty with his hands perhaps more clearly than he can see it with his eyes, and one can even sometimes enjoy a glass of inferior wine—if the thirst is there and nothing else is available.'

Pain needling through her, Sandra retorted, 'You don't pretend I'm more than a stopgap, yet you have to rely on me almost entirely. For someone as defenceless as you,' she added sharply, 'you have either a rare courage or a vast stupidity!'

'I'm never defenceless, girl, so don't fool yourself.'

'Neither am I, Mr Freeman!'

He laughed with lazy cruelty. 'I'm quite aware that the small cat scratches, but so much more enjoyable is the taming of such a creature. But haven't I warned you before about calling me Mr Freeman? A slip of the tongue like that on Corfu and my grandmother will pounce like a hawk. Perhaps I should say a ton of bricks, as you would indeed be crushed to death by the weight of her disapproval.'

'A nice lot you are!' Sandra cried.

'As you may well find out,' he rejoined sarcastically.

Next day, on the four-engined Boeing jet, heading for
Corfu, Sandra found herself going over the events of the
previous evening. Not that it made very exciting reminis-
cence, but odd things jerked her memory. After tea Stein
had given her ten minutes to change before the arrival of
a luxurious hired car. In it he had directed the driver, in
fluent Greek, to take them to the Acropolis.

'You must see that,' he'd said dryly, 'otherwise your
friends might refuse to believe you'd been to Greece.'

The Acropolis stood out above the city, but he wouldn't
allow her to explore alone. Nor did he feel, he said, like
fighting his way blindly through the crowds. One day, he
had promised, he would show her properly, and she had
had to be content, although she had had a crazy desire to
take his hand and lead him up through the gardens to the
top of the hill. Knowing exactly what he would think of
such a plan if voiced, she had remained silent, crouched in
her corner of the smoothly murmuring car which then
drove them to Piraeus, Athens' harbour. Two things Stein
pointed out, in complete contrast—the Acropolis, so dis-
tant and still, as if the hands of ancient Greek gods were
still laid upon it, and the harbour, with its shops and waterfront bustling with noise and life, where everything and
everyone seemed more than alive.

They didn't stay long. Stein's face had grown grim and
Sandra had found herself wondering if he had ever sailed.
There was so much about this man she didn't know, so
much she longed to find out, but as he had stood there,
his head turned towards the sun and sea, she hadn't dared
ask.

Later, at the hotel, he had asked her to find him something fairly formal to wear for dinner and told her not to
wait up as he didn't know what time he would be back.

Sorting his clothing had seemed so intimate a task that
she had been nervous that he might ask her to do more.

She had been even more frightened that he might, perhaps mistakenly, invade her bedroom when he returned in those early hours, which could so sway the emotions. Moonlight over the beauty that was Greece, she suspected, might be powerfully potent. But she had fallen asleep almost straight away, in spite of her apprehension, the worst she had to deal with being Stein's derisive grin at breakfast that morning, as if he had known all about the fears which had beset her and was amused by them.

# CHAPTER FOUR

About an hour later they landed on Corfu, at the international airport by the Ionian Sea. Here they were met by a large car and Sandra, who had been expecting having to wait for a taxi, gazed at it in surprised relief. The man who drove it, while not in uniform, had the unmistakable air of a professional chauffeur.

'*Kyrie!*' Leaving the car, he came quickly towards them, speaking to Stein.

'*Thimios?*' The two were obviously old friends. They embraced in the typical Greek fashion before Stein turned back to where Sandra stood uncertainly.

'Sandra, come and meet my grandmother's right-hand man.' He introduced her to Thimios. 'My secretary, fiancée, Miss Weir.' Sandra noticed how he added fiancée last!

She liked Thimios's old-fashioned bow, although she didn't quite know what to make of it, or what to say. His brown eyes twinkled in a brown-skinned face which reminded Sandra of the softest tanned leather, and she smiled.

Thimios must have been satisfied with her tentative smile, for he bowed again, as if in approval. 'If the *thespinis* will come this way——' he led Stein and her across to the waiting car.

'Thimios has been with my grandmother longer than I can remember,' Stein told her as they roared off with an over-extravagance of tooting and screeching brakes. 'He used to hook me out of the sea before I could walk. It must be due to him that I'm still here.'

'Then you have a lot to be grateful for.' Sandra smiled gently at Thimios's dark head bent over the wheel.

'Perhaps!' Stein exclaimed harshly. 'But I might have reason yet to wish he'd let me drown. Now I can't even see the waters he saved me from.'

Sandra drew a quick breath. She could scarcely accuse him of self-pity, because there was none in his voice, but she was already aware of his black moods and had come to fear them, for he treated any indication of sympathy with obvious contempt. While she longed to comfort him he wouldn't allow it. Wasn't he always warning her that he wanted nothing of her thoughts or pity! Hadn't he just emphasised this again, perhaps more for her benefit than Thimios's, when he had introduced her first as his secretary. She must occasionally endure the brunt of his savage, Greek-like passion, but that was all!

Shaken, she groped her way through a maze of varying emotions, trying to find a few impersonal words. 'Perhaps one day you might recover your eyesight, Stein. Then you might also regain a reason to be grateful that Thimios saved your life.'

She wasn't prepared that he should find her hand, crushing it until she cried out. They were going through Corfu town and Thimios didn't seem to hear her whimper of distress.

Stein had apparently been waiting for it and with harsh laughter flung her hand back to the padded upholstery. 'Stop parroting such glib remonstrations, girl, or you might find I can hurt even more.'

'I hate you!' She shrank back into her corner, swallowing hard to control the sobs which were making her throat ache.

Unerringly his hand came out, this time to find the tear on her pale cheek. Contemptuously he flicked it. 'I prefer a healthy hate, my dear, to a dishonest pretence of caring.'

They left Corfu town with its high-rise flats and hotels behind, making for the north-west coast. They swept through small Greek villages with plain little shops set on narrow streets. They ran between orange and olive groves, past rugged bays and promontories with the road growing rougher as they travelled further north. There was a fat little woman sitting on a donkey, looking as if she had all the time in the world to reach her destination, but otherwise very little sign of any other life. Above them loomed the cypress-covered hills and below them the glass-smooth water of the Ionian Sea. The pink of the oleander blended with the silver plumage of olive trees to give a certain beauty to the villages which grew fewer and lonelier as they went along. It amazed Sandra that many of these seemed to be perched halfway up the mountain sides, until Stein told her it was because of pirates who until well into the nineteenth century had raided the coast. To protect themselves the villagers had been forced to build their homes where they might see the raiders approaching.

Half an hour later they took a precarious bend and turned off the main road to approach, along a narrow track, a large white villa. Standing out against the cypress-shrouded mountain on a rocky ridge above a narrow piece of land dotted prettily with olive trees, it looked as if it was literally clinging to the mountain side. Below, far off in the deep blue water of the sea, lay a large yacht, but otherwise, as in the villages they had passed, there was no sign of any inhabitants. Their isolation seemed complete and rather frightening.

Thimios opened the car door with a flourish when they stopped. 'I'll see to your luggage,' he bowed. 'I expect Madame will be waiting.'

'Come along, Sandra,' Stein said coolly, pausing to wait for her by the door. 'I don't want you cringing along at my heels like an island cur. My grandmother will expect a girl of some spirit.'

Silently Sandra trembled. 'You're despicable,' she whispered in fierce undertones, 'and I refuse to let you tread me into the earth. I'm actually beginning to believe Alexandra could be well rid of you!'

She thought, from the expression on his face, she had gone too far, but she was glad that instead of her usual despair she felt nothing but cold anger. It gave her the strength to ignore the low sentence he muttered beneath his breath and stiffened her suddenly weak limbs against the possibility of his ever carrying out his low-voiced threats.

His grandmother's villa was a revelation, though, judging by the car, Sandra had realised the old lady must have considerable wealth. The house was luxurious and surprisingly modern in its furnishings. By contrast Madame Kartalis was tall, grey-headed and austere.

Unlike Thimios she didn't choose to welcome Sandra with a smile but stared her up and down from eyes a shade darker than Stein's and just as inhibiting.

She gazed at Sandra hard after greeting Stein fondly. 'So this is the woman you are affianced to, my grandson?'

'Yes.' Stein's reply was brief, not noticeably enthusiastic, Sandra noted dully.

'But she is scarcely a woman, Stein. I will venture to suggest she is little more than a child. Far too young for you!'

He shrugged. 'It is little use going on about the difference in our ages, grandmother. I am scarcely in my dotage and the deed is done.'

'I had hoped,' the old lady seemed to forget Sandra was there, 'that you would marry one of your Greek cousins. Now your blood will be further diluted—if this girl is capable of giving you the sons you crave.'

This proved too much for Sandra. Her cheeks flamed and she couldn't refrain from cutting in. 'I'm sure Stein won't mind if I don't have a family, madame. It's something I haven't yet decided.'

There was a moment's awful silence which Sandra tried deliberately to ignore by staring around the large, opulent salon, at the beautiful examples of Grecian pottery, the rugs spread richly on the marble floor. Stein was angered, she realised, by her statement. Gradually, over the past hours, he had seemed to grow more Greek than English and this was a land where men still generally dominated their women. Or had he been like this all along and it had only taken the background atmosphere to make her fully aware of it?

Then he said, coldly furious, 'Sandra, you will be shown to your room.' He gestured towards the black-clad servant who lurked in the shadows. 'I would advise you to go with Katrina. She is the wife of Thimios, so you will be well looked after.'

Her heart beating quickly, Sandra made no effort to obey. She was conscious that he considered his orders not to be disputed, especially in front of his grandmother, and if she refused to do as he commanded he might lose a certain face. Nevertheless she was unable to drag herself in the direction he indicated but instead stood glaring at him, momentarily forgetting he couldn't see.

'I don't feel tired, or like going to my room,' she retorted stubbornly. 'I'd much rather take a walk, perhaps by the sea.'

'You will do as you're told!' he thundered, while his grandmother stood silently by, her eyes cool as steel but looking as if she derived much enjoyment from their less than loving duel.

Unhappily, her new-found courage fading a little, Sandra stood biting her lip, wishing she dared go on defying him. How could Stein Freeman make her tremble and obey when all she had to do was turn her back on him? Perspiration touched her white brow and the deeply shadowed cleft between her breasts which had once known the exploratory touch of his lean fingers.

Madame spoke triumphantly. 'When it comes to the question of a family you will be left with little choice, Miss Weir. Stein is a man who could beat any woman into submission.'

Stein's lip curled in agreement. 'Sandra has already

felt the weight of my disapproval on more than one occasion, Grandmother. She knows better than to try me too far, and you will no doubt forgive her if she sometimes seems indiscreet. Possibly later you might give her a few words of advice?'

What an absolutely hateful old woman! Sandra thought bitterly after Thimios's wife had left her in her bedroom. Feeling unhappily exhausted, she gazed about her, all the pleasure she had felt in her surroundings fading rapidly. Madame Kartalis had been openly antagonistic, deliberately and spitefully introducing a subject which might have been embarrassing between intimate friends. She had stared at Sandra's narrow hips as if she had been a brood mare and found sadly wanting.

That Stein had allowed it, not turning a hair when his grandmother had coolly insulted her, seemed even more reprehensible. After all, she was supposed to be his fiancée! Uneasily Sandra wandered to the window, staring out over the olive groves, pale green and silver, to the sea. There had been such a hard gleam to his eyes as they had rested on her that she had found it difficult to believe he was really blind, and so helpless.

Suddenly stricken with remorse, Sandra clutched her hand to her mouth and, with a dismayed gasp, she was across the room and downstairs again before she quite realised. She must find Stein! How quickly she forgot his condition. He was in need of help, not anger and resentment, no matter how he provoked her. Wasn't it a sign of weakness that he just needed to make her furious and all her good resolutions seemed to disappear?

There was no one in the great hall, so she ran into the salon hoping to find him there. He wasn't to be seen, but Madame Kartalis was still there, regally upright on her hard chair, the impact of her black intent gaze bringing Sandra up short. The shock of that hard-eyed regard went right through Sandra, making her shiver.

'I'm looking for Stein,' she faltered, brushing back her flying hair with one hand. 'He could need my help.'

'Come here, child!' the harsh voice, which still retained an effective degree of strength for all her great age, seemed to encircle Sandra, drawing her in spite of herself.

'I was looking for Stein,' she repeated.

'How could you help him?' Madame asked coldly as Sandra drew nearer. 'I am told you are typing his new book, but he surely is not bothering with that just now?'

'No,' Sandra agreed nervously, 'not right at this moment, madame.'

'Then what did you hope to do for him, Miss Weir?'

Sandra felt her cheeks go red but returned the old lady's stare defiantly. 'I—I thought he might need help with his clothes? In the hotel——'

'Yes?' Madame's eyes were beady as she paused and, too late, Sandra recalled Stein's advice.

'Nothing,' Sandra's voice faltered guiltily. 'I merely helped him find the right shirt.'

'I see.' Madame's voice went even icier with disapproval. 'I suppose, being a foreigner, you have no shame! You stay in one of the best known establishments in Athens and help my grandson to dress.' Distractedly she flung up her claw-like hands. 'What are my friends to say to this! We will be the subject of ridicule all over the island and beyond. Hadn't I hoped he would marry a virgin? We Greeks set much store by this and a man of Stein's standing usually chooses wisely. I hadn't fully realised the pitfalls for someone who has lost his sight.'

'Please!' Sandra's eyes went huge in her white face as a wave of despair shook her. Dear God, did she need such an enemy? Surely Madame didn't have to judge her like this, pronouncing her in the wrong when she scarcely knew her? 'I've told you, I only helped with his clothes!'

'Well, you won't have to do even that while you are here, girl,' the old lady said tartly. 'Thimios is looking after him, so please confine yourself to your own quarters. Remember, if a man loses his respect for a girl he may also lose his desire to marry her. We have beautiful girls on this island who would make him a much more suitable wife.'

'Yes, madame!' Her exclamation of agreement far from servile, Sandra turned without another word and ran swiftly back to her own room.

Dinner was a quiet affair. They dined late and Sandra, who hadn't caught sight of Stein since they had arrived, felt an overwhelming surge of relief to see him walking towards her, his confident stride never faltering until he stood by her side.

'I don't know how you manage,' Madame spoke abruptly, as they went into the dining room. 'You never put a foot wrong.'

'That's because I know this house like the back of my hand and I remembered you never change the furniture around.' He shot an amused glance at Sandra. 'I have also reason to be grateful to Sandra. She wears always a distinctive, flower-like perfume. It's perhaps my good fortune that it appears to be the only one she has.'

Sandra bit her lip hard. 'It was given to me by my last employer when I left. I'm fond of it,' she added defensively.

'Then I shall have to buy you some other.' Stein's softer mood dispersed curtly. 'I don't fancy having my fiancée saturated by another man's gift.'

Madame said quickly, ignoring this little aside, 'You will feel better after you've been with me a few weeks, Stein. You were brought up here and familiar surroundings are usually comforting.'

When Stein made no reply she continued, with a sharp glance in Sandra's direction at the other side of the long table. 'Already, Stein, after a few short hours you look more relaxed. My house and my presence will probably do you more good than your fiancée, who possibly imagines to do so by dressing up in something ridiculously flimsy and brushing her hair loose like a wanton. Can't you restrain it, girl?'

'I—it's not very long,' Sandra replied carefully, trying desperately to keep her voice even. Whatever happened she must not allow Madame to provoke her to anger. Her dress was thin, but the night was warm and she was sure it wasn't suggestive, as Madame seemed to imply.

'I believe you are an actress or something?' Madame's voice implied that this was something less than desirable.

Sandra's face paled with apprehension. She didn't know what to say, not knowing what Stein had told his grandmother. 'There was only one film,' she faltered.

'What colour is your dress, Sandra?' Stein cut in, his hand pausing on the fine old silver, as if in two minds whether or not to come to her rescue.

'Green,' Madame laughed coldly without giving Sandra a chance to speak. 'Green like her cat's eyes, and it barely covers her smooth shoulders. Not that I perhaps need tell you how smooth they are,' she said acidly, 'when you have already stayed together in Athens.'

Stein smiled, if anything seeming to enjoy his grandmother's outrageous conversation and having little regard for Sandra's almost palpable agitation. He quoted, as he had once done before to Sandra, 'Being blind doesn't, in some ways, make me any less of a man, Grandmother. And Sandra is not a Greek.'

'That I realise!' The old voice was heavily accentuated. 'How long have you been betrothed?'

'Some time.' As if he could actually see Sandra's flaming cheeks he taunted diabolically, 'Too long—months!'

'Months?' Noisily enjoying her soup, Madame shrugged. 'And you have never been a patient man, Stein.'

'No,' he agreed, his eyes glinting.

Still hot-cheeked, Sandra kept her long lashes lowered on the sparkling crystal. They talked as though she wasn't there and, because of her real position in Stein's life, she wasn't able to get up and walk out as she would liked to have done. She had never met anyone with quite such a sharp tongue as Madame Kartalis and found her frankness increasingly disconcerting. Even now she was continuing.

'I remember, Stein, when you fell in love with Sophy and would have her right away. You had been gone from Corfu some years then and had forgotten a Greek girl's reticence.'

Her pulse jerking painfully, Sandra glanced quickly at Stein, but met only the mocking smile on his mouth.

As if hearing her sharply indrawn breath, he answered coolly, 'As one grows older one learns that a more subtle approach is wiser. In the end it usually accomplishes the same thing just as swifty.'

Madame frowned, as if about to favour her grandson this time with one of her censorious retorts, but Katrina entered followed by a maid carrying dishes of rich veal flavoured distinctively with herbs. There was, to Sandra, a welcome silence while plates were removed and replaced, but it did not last long. As soon as the servants had gone again, Madame began talking again.

'You won't mind, Stein, if I invite a few younger people while you are here? So many of our friends have enquired about you since your accident. I fear they will be offended if I don't tell them of your presence here.'

'Yes, ask who you like,' he agreed suavely, without consulting Sandra, 'Only remember, Grandmother, I have work to do.'

The old lady's shoulders lifted, as though this was the last consideration. 'It is better that you relax for a while.'

Stein smiled lightly, turning his dark head towards her across the table. 'Will Sophy be coming with the rest?' he asked blandly.

'Yes, yes.' Madame reached out approvingly and tapped his fingers, 'She is still unmarried and, I suspect, retains a fondness for you. In fact it is she who has been enquiring most.'

'Such concern I indeed find comforting,' he nodded,

casting a derisive glance at Sandra. 'I receive so little of it. Maybe I could do with more evidence of affection.'

'I didn't think you would welcome being fussed over so obviously,' Sandra couldn't help retorting waspishly.

'Oh,' he said, speaking softly, 'I imagine I could stand it.'

After the meal he sat drinking coffee and talking to his grandmother, and as their conversation was mostly in Greek, Sandra was unable to join in. Not that she really wanted to as Madame's tongue, when addressing her, merely seemed to get sharper and Stein's apparent indifference hurt, but, she thought wistfully, it might have been nice to have been included in some more general topics than those they had discussed. She imagined Madame was asking questions about Stein's accident as his expression was sometimes remote, as if he kept his patience with difficulty. Sandra recalled the same cool mask whenever she herself had dared to broach the same subject.

Yet, for all she was excluded from their talk, she found herself listening with pleasure to his deep voice and watching him furtively beneath her lashes. This latter was becoming a habit and it bewildered her to realise there were times when she couldn't seem to keep her eyes off him, never tiring of his rugged face, his strong, tall body.

The lights swayed slightly in the gentle breeze coming in through the window and, as it played on his face, Stein rose to his feet. 'I'd like a word with you, Sandra, before you go to bed. We dine late here, as you know, and already it is almost midnight.' His fingers lightly touched his Brailled watch.

'Yes, of course.' She went curiously to his side, wondering what he could have to discuss with her at this hour.

'Perhaps we might take a stroll in the moonlight? Thimios tells me the moon is full, so you should be able to see where we are going.'

The dryness in his voice not going unheeded, Sandra followed him out after saying a polite goodnight to his grandmother.

The old lady was about to retire. Katrina was waiting to escort her to bed and from the way in which she was shaking her head, Sandra guessed it was long past Madame's usual bedtime. Stein kissed his grandmother gently.

There was scent in the garden from the flowers and the cypress trees. The sun had long since gone down and the air was cooler. Below them, as they wandered to the edge of the isthmus, not a ripple disturbed the surface of the bay, and above, as Thimios had promised, the moon sailed in full splendour.

'You must have known of the moonlight in Athens last night?' Sandra said suddenly, very aware of his hand thrust through her arm, holding her to his side. 'You were late getting in.'

'So you noticed?'

'No, of course not!' It was the truth that she had been asleep when he had got back, but she needn't tell him of the long hours she had lain awake listening for him, wondering anxiously if he was all right, wondering even more feverishly if it was a woman who kept him out so late. 'Why did you want to see me alone?' she asked quickly.

'I wanted to ask you to be pleasant to my grandmother,' he rejoined mildly. 'She is getting old and doesn't always consider what she says.'

Was this a kind of apology? If only she could be sure! 'I try to be pleasant,' she said stiffly, making a futile effort to ease away from him. If they were going to have another quarrel she could conduct her side of it better with a little distance between them.

'I don't believe you've tried very hard,' he retorted.

The unfairness of this smote Sandra harshly. Even with allowances for Madame's great age she was still an old devil! Anger freed her tongue impulsively as she swung around to him. 'Listen, Stein, I came here against my will but prepared to be friendly with all your relations. How can it be my fault that your grandmother seems to have taken an unfair dislike to me, an aversion you deliberately seem to be fostering! All the time she was accusing me of not being able to give you a dozen children you just stood by, letting her say what she liked!'

He looked down on her from his great height, his face hardening. 'It was quite obvious that you found even the thought of having my children repulsive. No man would welcome that.'

Gulping, her heart beating so much faster, Sandra felt trapped, as much by the sheer force of her own emotions as what he said. 'There's a time and place for everything,' she managed weakly.

His eyebrows lifted indifferently. 'But for someone of my grandmother's age time and opportunity can be limited. This is possibly why she is so outspoken. Also she worries, naturally, that I might not have a son and heir.'

'I notice,' Sandra burst out bitterly, 'how you always consider your family and yourself, never me!'

Grimly his hands came up to grasp her. 'So you feel sorry for yourself, Miss Weir? Why should I give you sympathy and help? Did either you or Alexandra ever consider me?'

Sandra's voice rose as tremors ran through her. 'Why do you always drag this up? Surely I've paid a thousand times over for Alexandra's sins? How you do like your pound of flesh!'

'I don't consider you've paid anything like enough, my dear.' His voice was so deadly quiet she trembled with a sudden terror. 'Your cousin was at fault, but your deception is the greater. It was you who turned the situation into a pantomime and must be prepared to pay the price. Last night I almost decided to return early and visit you in your bed, but no such torture is effective if applied too quickly—none, that is, but the final culmination. But until then, I have vowed to take my time with you, so you will know what it is like to suffer.'

'Stein!' As the leashed savageness of his rage swept over her she struggled desperately. 'Let me go! Losing your eyesight has maddened you!'

'Perhaps,' he agreed, dragging her closer, so that her dress tore.

'If you could only see,' she sobbed, 'you would realise!'

'I can't see, damn you! Only my senses can do that for me.' He caught her to him with a hungry, angry urgency which she couldn't escape. Ruthlessly he tore the narrow strap from off one of her shoulders and buried his lips in the hollow against the bone. 'I can feel, and if this has to be enough, so far as you're concerned, you little cheat, I'm willing to settle for it.'

Dismayed, Sandra tried to move, but felt her bones and muscles were dissolving to jelly and, as the pressure of his mouth deepened on her warm skin, she became conscious of the clamour of her blood that demanded she make no continuing objection to being crushed in his arms. To struggle seemed only to entice him further. He twisted her into the angle of one arm, where she couldn't move, holding her in an angry yet sensual grip, while one hand wandered down the small of her back to pull her tightly against him. Then she felt his firm touch moving over her half bared breasts.

'You little impostor!' he muttered thickly as, fighting the lustful feelings he aroused in her, she tried again to push him away. 'Don't tell me you're indifferent. That I won't believe. How many men have you been with, I wonder?'

'None!' she gasped, hating him.

Even his hard, sceptical laughter hurt. 'No honesty anywhere,' he muttered, his head dropping to follow the direction of his hand.

As she felt the rough grate of his chin over her sensitive flesh she gave a strangled gasp. 'Stein!' his name came out on an agonised breath. 'You don't know what you're doing to me!'

'Don't I?' his voice took on a low note dryness. 'You must take me for a fool, sweetheart.'

Again she tried to tell him to stop, but before she could speak his mouth was on hers, his lips hot against her lips and, as a lascivious surge of answering passion swept through her, she closed her eyes against the moon swaying dizzily.

It was some time before he raised his head and suddenly thrust her away. 'Enough!' he said brutally.

Shaking, feeling as though she were on fire, Sandra drew back instinctively as his arms fell from her. 'Never do that again—I hate it!' she choked, hating herself more that she dared not admit the truth—that all she really wanted was to be back in his arms. Silently to herself she acknowledged this. He had some hold on her, some tenacious emotional grip on her senses that could yield her totally helpless against him, but she would rather die than let him know.

'Come,' he was saying harshly, you're only convincing yourself, although I doubt if you're succeeding to do even that! Can you manage to lead me back through the gardens? I can't be expected to remember every stick and stone out here and you can be grateful I couldn't trust myself to carry you to the nearest grassy hollow. Whoever heard of a would-be lover falling over his feet?'

Once more she had to endure his hold on her arm and bite her bruised lips against the tremors his words sent through her. Was this, she wondered dully, the peculiar mystery of seducement? She had looked at him and something within her had responded immediately to his virile, animal-like attraction, quickening her pulse and breath in a way she would never have believed possible. And it wasn't the expression in his eyes which excited her, because he couldn't see. This was something, she realised, she would have to fight, if it wasn't to lead to heartache, but she wished dearly that she knew how.

'Tomorrow morning,' Stein instructed, as they reached

the house, 'you will come to my study. Thimios will show you where it is, and we will begin revising my first chapter. Please be there on time.'

'I thought you weren't going to start work again until you were on your island?'

His voice dealt impatiently with the uncertainty in hers. 'Do I employ you to do as you're told or not?'

Sandra's hands clenched as she tried to steel herself not to notice his sarcasm. 'I don't want your grandmother to think I'm encouraging you to go against her wishes. You do look tired.'

'Perhaps you are the one who tires me,' he sneered, 'with your pretence of virtuous reluctance. Oh, and by the way,' he paused, looking back over his shoulder as he left her, 'we'd better act a bit more lover-like in my grandmother's presence. If she were to discover the truth I would have even less peace than I have now.'

The next morning Sandra rose early after a restless night and decided to explore the beach. Stein had warned her not to try and swim on her own as the beach here shelved steeply into the sea and, apart from this, the water in April could still be quite cold. She would be wiser, he had added, to stick to the pool in the garden behind the house.

This morning, however, Sandra felt the turbulence of the sea would more match her mood than a flaccid, man-made pool, and it was with some determination that she searched for the way to the beach. To her surprise she couldn't find any kind of path down through the rocks. Last night the beach had looked so near; now she saw this wasn't so and that the cliff face might be dangerous. Eventually, throwing discretion to the winds, she began scrambling downwards, recklessly disregarding the stones and crags covered with sharp edges and spiky plants, until she arrived at her goal.

Once on the beach she stared at the cuts and scratches on her pale hands with a resigned shrug. Freshly made, they were not as painful as they might be later, but she resolved to forget about them. After all, on such a beautiful morning, what were a few scratches? Turning, she gazed back up the hillside, where the wild spring flowers of Greece lay like a carpet, and wondered how such beauty could conceal such a treacherous terrain. More despondently she wandered a little way along the beach before ruefully climbing back up the almost vertical face. At the top it was no comfort to discover her dress almost as torn as her hands. In future she would stick to her jeans for such expeditions, otherwise, what with one thing and another, she was going to have very few dresses left!

To her despair it was much later when she got back to her bedroom than she had thought, and her heart sank when she surveyed the true damage to her hands and wondered what Stein would say. He couldn't see, but if she was unable to type properly then there was every chance he might find out. Quickly she washed the deep cuts in warm water, but had nothing to apply to them, and no time now to seek out Thimios or Katrina to beg some ointment which might soothe them.

As best as she could she changed into a fresh dress, pushing her soiled one out of sight. She had no idea of laundry arrangements at the villa but didn't want to bother anyone about this on her first day. Katrina must have enough to do with extra people to look after.

In the study, to which a hovering Thimios directed her, she found Stein waiting, with his usual impatience. For a long moment she gazed at him, not really hearing when he derided her for being late. He wore dark slacks with a white shirt. The trousers fitted his hips and strong thighs closely and were belted neatly to his lean waist. A cold thrill stiffened Sandra's spine as she remembered how it had felt to be held close to him, to feel her own slender limbs pressed tight against his taut muscles,

'I'm sorry,' she said at last, conscious he was waiting for

some explanation, 'I'll try not to be late in future.'

'Please do,' he warned coldly, picking up his first chapter which he wanted to revise. 'I would like you to read this back to me and make a note of any changes in the margin. Afterwards you might have to retype some pages, but I hope not all.'

'As you like,' Sandra agreed nervously, trying to ignore her stinging hands.

'You have a delightful speaking voice,' he went on abstractedly. 'I believe it would be a good idea if you were to record each chapter as we go along. Then I need simply play it back for the final revision, as by the time the book is finished you probably won't be with me any more.'

# CHAPTER FIVE

As Stein spoke Sandra felt her cheeks pale as she remembered the old saying that fate has a nasty habit of giving us what we think we most desire. Two weeks ago all she had wanted was to escape this man, but now she only longed to stay with him and, to her shame, had through the night thought she might be willing to do so in any capacity he demanded.

This morning, as his harsh words speared through her, she felt herself flinch while even yet being unable to accept that she could have come to care so much in so short a time.

She nodded silently as, when the silence continued, he asked if this would suit her. Then, realising he couldn't see, she said hastily that it would, adding, 'If you think I can manage?'

'Naturally. If I hadn't thought so I wouldn't have suggested it,' he replied tersely, and she sensed his impatience was not so much with her as his changed circumstances which forced him to work this way.

'It's an awful shame!' she burst out, her voice thick with tears of pity.

'Sandra, for heaven's sake!' he snapped. 'Haven't I told you before I don't want your pity? As it is, your sympathy is probably only prompted by a guilty conscience and that kind of condolence is no good to me or anyone. Now, if you're quite finished trying to impress me with tears, might we make a start? For a secretary you've a bit too much to say.

Thereafter they worked steadily, but when Thimios knocked on the door two hours later, Sandra sensed his relief.

'Guests have arrived,' Thimios informed Stein. 'Madame wishes you to come to the salon.'

'Very well.' Stein made no protest at such an imperious summons but evidently had no intention of asking Sandra to accompany him. 'You'd better start retyping those half dozen pages,' he instructed. 'I'll see you at lunch.'

Lunch? Sandra shrugged ruefully, as the door closed behind him and she recalled, although it had been no one's fault but her own, that she hadn't yet had breakfast. Nor had she had so much as a cup of coffee, and suddenly she longed for one. In fact she doubted if she could begin to work again without one. Her fingers were now stinging so fiercely it might be difficult to type, and she felt rather sick.

Greatly daring, she pressed the bell and to her surprise Thimios came almost immediately. She had thought he might be looking after the visitors. 'You wanted me, Miss Sandra?'

'Yes,' the friendliness in his voice comforted her oddly, 'I wondered if I might have some coffee and perhaps a biscuit?'

His brown eyes were anxious. 'You didn't eat breakfast, but Katrina says, when I speak of it, that English ladies today often do not.'

Sandra smiled ruefully and she could see he thought she agreed, but better this than that he should guess the truth. In the morning she would have to pretend her appetite had been miraculously restored.

When he returned with a tray a few minutes later, she thanked him warmly but gave a start of dismay when he noticed her hands. Silently she blessed herself for not remembering to keep them out of sight. 'It's nothing to worry about, Thimios. I scratched them on the cliffs when I was out earlier. Perhaps Katrina has a little ointment she could let me have?'

Thimios frowned and hurried away and when he came

back Stein was with him. Immediately Stein ordered her
to let him see her now hidden fingers.

Knowing very well what he meant, she threw Thimios
an angry look as she jumped clumsily to her feet, thrusting
her hand into the pockets of her cotton dress.

It was foolish trying to evade him. With a muttered
expletive he was beside her, with an accuracy of direction
which amazed her, grasping her tightly before his fingers
moved with surprising gentleness over hers.

But there was nothing compassionate about his voice.
'Where did you do this?'

'If Thimios,' she cast a despairing glance at the hovering
servant, 'has already told you so much, I don't know why
he hasn't told you that. I climbed down to the beach.'

She felt Stein stiffen, saw his mouth clamp. 'I don't have
to believe this! You mean you went down there this
morning, on your own, before coming in here?'

'Yes. I shouldn't have been late, only I couldn't find the
right track.'

'You had only to ask.'

'But there was no one.'

'You could have come to me. I suppose, as usual, you
couldn't bring yourself to ask my help?'

Their exchange was so sharply bitter, Sandra found herself wincing wretchedly. 'How did I know where to find
you? You might have been in bed.'

'Do you imagine you would have suffered more harm
if you'd joined me there? You might have enjoyed an hour
or two in my arms—eventually. Your hurt could have been
of a different kind, and not as bad as this.'

Uncontrollably she quivered. How could he be so frankly
brutal, especially in front of Thimios? Then she saw
Thimios wasn't there. 'Where is he?' she faltered.

'Anticipating my wishes,' Stein said curtly. 'Hot water
and plasters, perhaps a bandage for this,' his finger-tip
paused over the deepest cut on her index finger. 'I'm

afraid you won't be able to type for a few days. A less benevolent employer couldn't be blamed for thinking you had done this deliberately.'

'Don't be stupid!' She felt so upset she scarcely knew what she was saying. 'Why should I try to injure myself on purpose when as soon as your brilliant book is finished I'll be free? Besides, I've only suffered a few scratches. To hear you go on one would imagine I'd broken my arm!'

While she paused for breath he said coldly, 'Your opinion of my book, Miss Weir, doesn't surprise me. I understand your shallow mind.'

Suddenly she had such a deep feeling of shame his cynical reference to her intelligence went unnoticed. She deserved all he said. Knowing how difficult it must be for him to work at all she had allowed a thirst for revenge to prompt her to speak as she would never have dreamt of doing normally. His blindness was responsible for his ill temper and cutting remarks, but she had no such excuse.

'Stein,' she whispered, staring up at his taut face, 'oh, Stein, I am sorry. I didn't mean that your book is no good —you must know it—it promises to be splendid. Even I, with my—er—shallow mind, can see that after only one chapter. Please forgive me.'

His mouth curled as his punishing grip tightened, then swiftly he released her. 'I think the situation is getting a bit too melodramatic,' he grunted. 'I must be going wrong in the head when I allow a little nobody like you to get under my skin. Ah, here comes Thimios with the bandages.'

Not knowing which hurt most, his harsh words or the stinging antiseptic, Sandra surrendered weakly to Stein's expert ministrations. He seemed capable of assessing the exact treatment for each finger and the scratches on her arms, but for all his undoubted skill she was glad when he was finished.

'Lunch is about to be served,' he drawled, as Thimios removed the basin of hot water. 'You can comb your hair and come with me. Our visitors are staying and expect to meet my fiancée, so you had better be prepared to be quite charming to me.'

Lunch proved an ordeal Sandra soon longed to be over. Madame Kartalis presided over a table surprisingly lavish considering her new guests had arrived unexpectedly. Beforehand, Stein had introduced Sandra to a Madame Nikitiadis and her two daughters. Xenia, the oldest one, was married. Petrina, the other, was not and spent most of the time gazing adoringly at Stein. It seemed very apparent she had met him before and had pleasant if not tantalising memories. She was young, perhaps in her middle twenties, and very pleasant to look at. While not exactly filled with enthusiasm, Sandra felt relieved she wasn't the mysterious Sophy, whom Stein had enquired about the previous evening, and did her best not to notice that Petrina often seemed to find it necessary to lay a gentle hand on Stein's arm.

They asked why Sandra's hands were covered with plasters and when she told them, the girls wanted to know why she had been so keen to go down to the beach when dear Madame Kartalis had such a beautiful pool.

'I hadn't been to the sea in years. I had a sudden fancy, not to swim, just to see the waves breaking over the sands and feel the salt spray,' she explained awkwardly.

'But how sad!' Madame Nikitiadis exclaimed in her excellent English. 'I love the sea, I couldn't imagine being without it!'

Stein's grandmother, who had been listening to the conversation intently, put in with a frown, 'This film you were in, Sandra—surely I recall Stein writing that it was made on a famous beach in Nassau?'

'Some of it was shot in Florida Keys and the Bahamas,' Stein agreed smoothly, 'but Sandra wasn't on that location. She has been over the sea in a plane, but I suppose, as she says, she hasn't been actually beside it.'

As Sandra gazed down at her plate in confusion she wondered unhappily where it was all to end. Stein might not always be around to save her from her own stupidity, and this incident surely proved just how easy it was to make a mistake.

Petrina looked her over so closely she felt uncomfortable. 'You don't really look like a film star, Miss Weir. At least,' Petrina admitted reluctantly, 'you have lovely hair and a good figure, but you're different somehow from the stars I've seen. Don't you think so, Stein?'

'Sandra wasn't the leading lady, but she has distinct possibilities when it comes to acting, I believe.'

Trying to eat her lunch with strangely clumsy fingers, Sandra hated the hidden dryness in Stein's voice. Why didn't he come out into the open and denounce her frankly as a cheat?

'We are looking forward to seeing the film of Stein's book,' the elder girl smiled charmingly. 'It will be an additional interest to see you in it, Miss Weir. What kind of a part do you have?'

Stein laughed carelessly, though he looked faintly watchful. 'It would only spoil it for you should we tell. It was only a small part. Perhaps you won't even spot her.'

Sandra went hot and cold, weary of trying to keep a smile fixed on her stiff lips. This was worse than she had ever envisaged. If Stein's friends did see the film and discovered the truth, what then?

'It won't be on general release for some time,' Stein pointed out smoothly, as if sensing Sandra's hidden panic.

'No, of course not. We realise that,' Petrina took over quickly from her sister. 'All the same, you must be anticipating the event enormously, both of you.'

Sandra glanced at Stein so anxiously that Petrina flushed. 'Oh, I am so sorry,' she faltered unhappily, 'I quite forgot about Stein.'

As her voice trailed off Stein said lightly, 'Don't be embarrassed, Petrina. I find this harder to bear than people's very natural blunders. Who knows, by the time my film is shown a miracle might have happened, making it possible for me to see again.'

'Of course! Oh, I do hope so! But I am sorry, dearest Stein.' Careless of watching eyes, Petrina laid a caring hand on his arm, her fingers alive with sympathy.

Already somewhat aware that other women found him attractive, Sandra caught her breath as she waited for Stein's reactions. Her eyes widened as she saw him smile at Petrina warmly before lifting her hand gently to his lips. Sandra swallowed a lump in her throat with difficulty. Whenever she betrayed the least bit of compassion all she ever received was a sharp rebuke!

Before the visitors left the daughters entreated Stein to come down to the local taverna on the next evening. Sandra too, if her hands were better. They were sure she would enjoy it. And Mrs Nikitiadis asked them all to dinner the following Saturday.

Sandra had been so sure Stein wouldn't go to the taverna that she could only stare with surprise when, after dinner the following evening, he told her to go and find a wrap.

'Keep on your pretty dress,' he drawled. 'I get tired of jeans.'

'But——' she began, thinking the latter might be more suitable. Besides, when he couldn't . . .

'If you say once more I can't see, I'll strangle you, my *thespinis*! I still have all my senses and I like the feel of silk against a silken skin better than denim.'

'You ought to have been a poet,' she mocked recklessly.

'A man can't be all things,' he jeered back, 'no matter how hard he tries. All I can be at the moment, I'm afraid, is an aspiring writer and perhaps lover.'

Sandra's breath quickened, for all he sounded so matter-of-fact. He would be a good lover, she was sure, although she wasn't so certain he would be a faithful one, but the darkly passionate side of his nature she didn't doubt. Dully she was aware that, in some indefinable way, to hold her and make light love to her offered Stein some kind of welcome release from the darkness which surrounded him, but she shuddered to think how it might be when, with his emotions fully aroused, he demanded more.

If their visit to the taverna near Paleokastritsa was a success, Sandra wasn't so sure about Mrs Nikitiadis's dinner. In the taverna, a low sand-coloured building set almost on the beach, she had felt fairly relaxed. There had been lighthearted entertainment and a happy atmosphere prevailing. Sandra had been content enough to sit with a drink of the local ouzo, watching the dancing and listening to the conversation. Not that she could make much of this as she had even yet only picked up a few words in Greek, but if nothing else she had learnt the Greeks loved to talk and argue, and she enjoyed their animated expressions. It made quite a change from the more reserved face of the average Englishman.

In spite of his harshness over the past few days, Sandra felt happy that most of those here seemed to know Stein, or know of him. She felt an almost glowing sense of pride at the way in which he seemed to have overcome his previous reluctance to go out and renew old acquaintances. But he refused to join in the local dances, even when Petrina begged him. Nor, surprisingly enough, would he allow Sandra to dance with any of the numerous young men who asked her.

'You are supposed to be my fiancée,' he said curtly. 'You must stay with me, not because I can't manage alone, but because it is expected of you. Besides,' he growled, 'why should these young men, whose voices tell me they find you attractive, have what I can't have myself?'

So she stayed beside him, grateful that he appeared to need her for any reason at all, and when for a few moments he put his arm around her narrow waist and drew her close she felt dizzy with a mysterious kind of delight.

That the following Saturday evening was one she sub-consciously dreaded didn't really register until she was actually inside the house of Madame Nikitiadis.

Thimios, as usual, drove them and there were only Stein and herself in the back of the big car as his grand-mother had declined to come. On the way Stein said little, other than to snap out a few brief replies when Sandra spoke. He had been morose for days. Not even the fact that her fingers soon healed and she was able to type again seemed to cheer him. She thought their visit to the taverna had done him good, but if it had, the effect had soon worn off. It wasn't because of neglect, Sandra was certain. The telephone rang continually with invitations from all over Corfu and people came to the house all the time. Yet, daily, she could feel him retreating into an increasingly grim silence. They hadn't done any work now for days and she didn't know what to make of it. That his grandmother appeared to blame Sandra for Stein's terse, black moods was not very comforting!

When they arrived at the Nikitiadis house Sandra thought she understood at last what was making her un-easy. Sophy Parara was there. She had been unable to see Stein sooner, she said, as she had been indisposed since re-turning from America. Sandra saw immediately that Sophy Parara was no naïve girl like herself, but a beautiful and very assured woman. Beside her Sandra lasped into un-certain silence as she listened to her talking to Stein.

'I couldn't get home quickly enough when my mother told me you were here,' she purred, shooting sharp little glances at Sandra, which naturally she knew Stein couldn't see. 'Poor Stein,' she went on, 'I was devastated to learn of your accident and should have liked to have rushed to your side immediately. Of course, knowing your fiancée would be there, I was forced to restrain myself.'

'You would have been a great comfort,' he smiled.

Sandra stared at him, amazed that he hadn't changed the

subject abruptly. While not exactly encouraging Sophy he appeared to appreciate her concern.

'I hope you are feeling better yourself?' he enquired politely, still speaking to Sophy.

'Oh yes,' Sophy returned. 'It was nothing, and I just couldn't wait to see you. Actually,' she laughed, with cool triumph, 'I bumped into an old friend of yours—Professor Manoli, at a reception in New York on Upper East Side. He was telling me about your case, without giving away any professional secrets, of course, and . . .'

'Come out on the terrace for a few minutes, Sophy. You can tell me there,' Stein interrupted smoothly, linking her arm through his and ignoring Sandra. 'Madame Nikitiadis isn't down yet, and I'm sure she would excuse us. It's such a long time since I've seen you that we have a lot to talk about.'

Staring after them, Sandra felt both deserted and curious. What news had Sophy been about to impart so cheerfully, and why had Stein manoeuvred her so deviously outside? She was sure it must have been of some importance to have made him act so abruptly, in the middle of what Sophy had been saying. Or was it simply—Sandra's heart fluttered in dismay—that he couldn't wait to get Sophy to himself, perhaps to explain his bogus engagement?

Over dinner Sophy, as if to emphasise the re-establishment of some previous relationship with Stein, asked Sandra mockingly if she wasn't yet tired of living in Greece. 'You must feel a stranger among us?'

'No!' Not intending to reply so hotly, Sandra impulsively confessed, 'Well, sometimes I do.'

'There, you see,' Sophy's thick brows lifted. 'Feeling this way you can't be helping Stein so much. How long have you been engaged, Miss Weir?'

Desperately Sandra glanced to where Stein was conversing with Mr Nikitiadis further down the table. 'About a year, I think.'

'A year!' Sophy's laughter was full of hidden scorn.

'I cannot imagine Stein waiting so long for someone he loves.'

'You forget my accident, Sophy.' At last he condescended to come to Sandra's rescue. 'It has made a difference.'

'But your future is almost assured now, my dear,' Sophy's voice was puzzled. 'I should have thought you'd be brimming over with impatience—you were never any other kind of lover. Is this not so?' she appealed with a charming grimace to her aunt, who made disapproving noises and looked slightly embarrassed.

'Don't look so horrified,' with a pretence of affection Sophy teased her. 'In England love and marriage are discussed more freely every day. In Greece it is the same. It is only on the islands that we still hang on to outworn customs, but even here——' the elegant shrug of her shoulders completed what she left unsaid.

'Part of our island charm lies in our outworn customs, and I for one shouldn't like to see them changed,' Madame Nikitiadis retorted stubbornly.

Again Sophy merely shrugged. 'All the same, I'm sure Stein and Sandra won't be embarrassed if I ask them when the wedding is to be. Unless, Sandra,' Sophy's lip curled, 'since Stein's accident you have been trying to postpone it indefinitely?'

Almost Sandra gasped at such effrontery, not even feeling slightly mollified to hear Stein insisting lightly that it had been he who insisted Sandra should have time to be quite sure. 'We have both been through a rather traumatic experience and need a breathing space to adjust. Because of this we haven't yet fixed any date for our marriage. I might as easily change my mind as Sandra.'

As Stein adroitly took charge of the conversation, Sandra felt her cheeks grow pale. What she felt for him could only be infatuation—but whatever it was it hurt! To hear him talking like this was like having a knife turned in an open wound and she found herself wishing feverishly that she had known at the beginning what she had been letting herself in for. What compensation, she wondered bitterly, would Alexandra be prepared to dole out for a broken heart? This whole episode was growing more and more into something she didn't understand, nor was she altogether sure she wanted to.

Yet on the way home, for all her resentment against Sophy, she was shocked when Stein exclaimed savagely, 'I wish people would stop prattling on about marriage. They must think me a complete fool!'

Her teeth gritted against the pain, she said as coolly as she was able, 'I agree—about our marriage at least. Under the circumstances I expect it's only natural they should be interested. There is one easy solution.'

'Don't ask me to release you.' He didn't pretend not to understand what she was getting at. 'I've already told you how important this book is to me.'

The most important thing, she suspected, was to prove his ability to work and at the same standard. It was something, she sensed, that he must have reassurance on, and to complete his present book was the only foreseeable way he could find out. He had other business interests, but this was the most important to him. As she turned to him, her heart was once again wrung with a compassion she dared not utter.

'When my next book is finished and we return to London you'll be free to go,' he snarled, lying back against the upholstery, his profile presented to her, hard and formidable. 'I'm sure the few hours I ask you to work can't be very taxing.'

Her whole body cold, Sandra looked dully out of the window at the brilliant stars which seemed to reflect in the dark waters of the glinting sea. The blue Ionian Sea, beautiful and mysterious, not in any way reflecting Stein's regard for her. He made it too obvious that he disliked her intensely, and there was nothing beautiful about hate. How was it, when she so often wished to be all things to him, he didn't appear to feel even one scrap of affection for her?

'I'm sure,' she derided stiffly, 'Sophy would be more than willing to step into my shoes, should you ask her.'

She wilted under the sudden blaze in his eyes. 'What on earth has Sophy to do with it? I may have been a blind fool, even before my accident, but I don't wish to hear her name on your lips.'

The lips he mentioned went white. 'I wasn't insulting her! I was simply making a suggestion.'

'Then kindly allow me to run my own life. A woman of Sophy's charm doesn't have to slave over a typewriter.' His mouth twisted sardonically as he gripped both her wrists, hurting her. 'Haven't I everything here I need? A moderately efficient secretary and entrancing little fiancée, whose body usually betrays even her most straitlaced rantings.'

'I never win, do I!' she cried wildly, with a nervous glance at the back of Thimios's impervious head.

'You'd better realise it!' Stein grated coldly, pulling her quickly to him, his hands releasing her wrists to run slowly over her bare arms and shoulders. 'How pleasant you feel,' he murmured with a devilish softness. 'Silk against silk.' Suddenly, without warning, he bent his head to crush her mouth savagely beneath his.

Minutes later he spoke thickly against her quivering lips. 'This is the only way I can really see you, and I refuse to ask your forgiveness. It's so easy when I'm paying for it, anyway. Quite without the usual complications.'

'Stein!' Horrified though she was by his thickly muttered comments, it seemed she could deny him nothing when he held her in his arms. Perhaps he was right in what he said about her, but she couldn't seem to care. 'Stein,' she breathed again, 'must we be always fighting each other?'

But then they were back at the house and it was too late. As though he regretted the slight softening on his face, he drew away from her abruptly without bothering to reply as Thimios opened the car door. 'Goodnight,' he said coldly, the curtness in his voice dismissing her even before he turned away.

For the next two weeks life at the Villa Kartalis grew increasingly busier, but this was only socially. So far as Stein's writing went, little was actually accomplished. Not even a letter from his London publisher seemed to hurry things up. Sandra knew that because Stein was used to working straight on to the typewriter himself, he found it difficult to dictate in a way he found satisfactory, and sensing his frustration, she did everything she could think of to help him and eventually thought she was succeeding. It was difficult but not impossible, or it wouldn't have been if his grandmother had been willing to leave him in peace.

The doorbell and telephone rang continually and Madame Kartalis, with an energy that far belied her eighty odd years, entertained indefatigably. Relations between her and Sandra remained strained, but while the old lady took every opportunity to speak sharply to her there were occasions when she did address Sandra in an almost cordial manner.

There was no getting away from it, Sandra thought unhappily, Madame favoured Sophy Parara as a granddaughter-in-law, and she was quite honest about it. Sophy appeared to share the same sentiments as she spent hours of each day at the villa. She came into the study, persuading Stein so charmingly to go out with her that he seldom refused. They swam in the pool together and Sophy drove him around the island while Sandra was left behind to solve his rough dictation as best she could. Often she sat blindly, seeing only two people, Sophy and Stein, in each other's arms. Stein seemed to have forgotten all about his stipulation that he and Sandra should appear a loving couple. It soon became apparent that he never gave it another thought.

Once, when Sandra suggested tentatively that she wouldn't mind a trip around the island herself, he told her intolerantly to get Thimios to take her. He didn't intend being driven like a helpless invalid in his grandmother's huge limousine to please her or anybody else. Hadn't the locals plenty to gawp at without adding him to their list of curiosities?

Only once did she take his advice and went alone. Thimios, whether instructed by Stein or not, she didn't know, had offered to take her several times, and one day, after Stein had gone off with a smirking Sophy, Sandra decided to go to Corfu Town and have a look around.

Thimios, as a general guide, couldn't be bettered. He wouldn't say a word against Stein, whom he obviously rated highly, but he did put himself out to make up for what he perhaps privately considered the *kyrios*'s neglect of the charming little *thespinis*.

Close to Corfu Town he showed her the beautiful villa of Mon Repos where Prince Philip was born and then he circled around by the coast to show her the famous Mouse Island and its sister island of Vlacherna, both lying peacefully in the blue reflective waters of the bay. After this they followed the waterfront and into the old town. Here, close to the harbour, were the old Venetian parts of the town, the high-balconied buildings strung along narrow streets.

They left the car and though Thimios said he could easily hire a *monipo*—one-horse carriage—Sandra preferred to explore on foot. There was the red-roofed church of Aghios Spiridon, the island's patron saint, but she declined to look at his mummified remains, to be seen in a glass-topped coffin. But apart from this there was so much to see that the afternoon flew, and finished with a delightful wander around the little jewellery shops and boutiques. Here she bought, with her precious drachmas, a shawl for Madame Kartalis and small gifts for Katrina and Thimios. The whole town was so colourful she felt reluctant to leave it, and she rather envied the tourists whose time was their own.

When they returned Stein was back but there was no sign of Sophy. 'Well,' he mocked, almost as if he had been put out by her absence, 'have you sent all your postcards?'

'I didn't buy any as there's no one to send them to,' she retorted, then could have bitten her tongue out when he sneered,

'Little Orphan Annie! Pull the other one.'

'It happens to be true,' she retorted, feeling near to tears, though not, she was convinced, of self-pity. It must be because he spoke so sharply; she prayed she might grow a thicker skin. Quickly she tried to change the subject by asking if he, too, had enjoyed his day.

He grunted derisively. 'As good as I can expect. Why the devil I go at all I don't know. If it wasn't for Sophy ...'

He broke off abruptly and, as he had declared Sophy a forbidden topic, Sandra stubbornly refused to show interest. She thought she knew, anyway, and didn't wish to hear him extolling another girl's virtues.

He sighed, still impatiently, turning his dark head towards her again. 'So Corfu Town drew you out of your shell but you purchased no cards or presents. How long is it since you lost your parents?'

His last question was so unexpected she was startled, 'Years ago—I was about eight. Gran brought me up.'

'Is she still alive?'

Hadn't she told him? 'No, she's dead too.'

'And since then, you've done exactly as you've pleased, using your freedom unwisely rather than well.'

She knew better than to argue when he was in this kind of mood. It was very obvious something had happened to displease him. 'Do you want to get on with some work?' she asked carefully.

'Work!' There was no reward for her willingness in the harshness of his tones. 'Haven't you learnt yet that my kind of work isn't something you can pick up whenever there are a few spare minutes? I'm not in the mood. I probably wouldn't manage more than a couple of inferior sentences and the telephone would no doubt be ringing in the middle of them.'

His mouth tightened and she saw his face was pale under his tan, as if his outing had proved exhausting. His strength, his hard, well-proportioned body seemed to contradict this impression, yet Sandra thought the lines of strain around his mouth had grown deeper since they had come here.

'What are you wearing?' He jumped so quickly to another subject she started, momentarily afraid he was going to touch her. Somehow she felt if he did she couldn't bear it. Not after he'd spent the entire afternoon with Sophy while she had wandered alone.

'A cotton dress.' She described it briefly, hoping this would satisfy him.

'You aren't short of clothes,' he startled her again by commenting dryly. He made no attempt to come near her.

'No,' Sandra's mind was not on what she was saying, 'Alexandra gave me a lot. All I have.'

'You can't be serious?'

'Why not?' Again she regretted a lack of thought, but it couldn't be helped now. What did it matter, anyway?

His voice held contempt. 'You mean you used the money they bought you with to pay for the clothes you have now?'

'Stein!'

'Shut up, girl. Tomorrow we'll go to town together and I'll buy you a new wardrobe. Never let it be said my fiancée wore clothes procured in this way. Tomorrow you can think of some excuse and ask Katrina to get rid of these.'

Sandra felt chilled all over, sensing his renewed hostility. 'I can't see how it can be any better, taking things from you.'

'You wouldn't, girl, would you? It's the kind of mentality you have!'

If this was bad there was worse to come. Almost Sandra didn't go down to dinner. To feel mentally bruised was nearly as bad as being hurt physically—in fact when she had time to think about it she decided it was worse. Bruises on skin faded in time, but a heart that ached might never recover. As she pondered, unhappily reluctant to change, she remembered how kind Thimios had been and that he had confided his beloved Katrina was cooking something special for the evening meal. Rather than disappoint them she bathed and put on a simple dress before descending the wide staircase. Stein had been in one of his worst moods this afternoon, but she must make allowances. Learning to live in a world of perpetual darkness must be a terrible strain, especially when, as in Stein's case, it hit one in the prime of life. He did try, and the courage he usually showed seemed above average. She must try to remember this whenever she felt like fighting him.

# CHAPTER SIX

SANDRA, who had hoped that a good wine and the excellent food might help, gauged Stein's mood as still bad, even as they finished eating. This evening Katrina's *adjem pilafe*—lamb cooked in rice—had been wonderful, and afterwards she had served *baclava*, a sweet made with thin pastry, honey and nuts. Now, as they sat drinking the thick Turkish coffee and Madame Kartalis nibbled greedily from the dishes of rich Turkish Delight, Sandra wondered if her mention of Alexandra had been responsible for plunging him into such a dark depression. Or was it that in the course of his outing with Sophy he had discovered a fondness for the Greek girl that made his supposed engagement to Sandra both an obstacle and a nuisance?

Naturally Madame wanted to know exactly where he had been that day and how dear Sophy was. His answers were short to the point of rudeness and, while she was somewhat surprised that he should be so unusually curt with his grandmother, there was nothing to prepare Sandra for his eventual announcement.

'Grandmother, I have decided to go to Kalnos to finish my book. Maybe I should say get it started, as this seems to be something I am scarcely going to accomplish here.'

There was a sudden fraught silence and Sandra realised Madame was as startled and perhaps as dismayed as herself. She said something sharply in Greek, but when Stein glanced pointedly at Sandra she repeated it reluctantly in English, 'I don't think that is a good idea.'

'In this instance,' Stein stated firmly, 'although you might accuse me of insolence, your opinion cannot matter. While for several reasons I might prefer to stay here, I cannot neglect my work. God knows I might have to forgo everything else but my writing.'

Madame frowned. 'But, my grandson, I believe you could live quite comfortably without this, even if you never did another hand's turn in your life. Why exhaust yourself when it is not imperative?'

'It is to me, my dear.' Sandra saw his face grow grim as Madame argued. 'Money alone can come to be meaningless if there is nothing left in life but the spending of it.'

'Your philosophy, Stein, is beyond me,' Madame retorted tartly. 'Why are the young so restless?'

He smiled dryly at that. 'I am not in my teens or even twenties any more, so there is little use making senseless comparisons. And I would hardly describe a desire to work as being restless.'

As Madame Kartalis paused uncertainly, Sandra strove to get a word in. 'Stein, I must talk to you about this before——' she hesitated, glancing anxiously at his grandmother, 'before you make any final arrangements.'

'They are already made, darling!' he emphasised his endearment with a thread of sarcasm. 'Don't you start being awkward! I might pander occasionally to Grandmother because of her age, but I refuse to do the same for a girl scarcely more than twenty.'

Madame Kartalis, being Greek, and having lived for the greater part of her life in a land where men usually dominated, appeared to think nothing of his decisive dismissal of Sandra's request. She was, though, as Sandra had already learnt, very aware of the proprieties.

'I'm afraid, Stein,' she said slowly, 'what you contemplate is impossible. I have been reluctant to pass on some very sad news to you. Indeed, I had determined to spare you it altogether, until you were much better, anyway. Even now I scarcely know how ...'

Stein lifted his head to interrupt her angrily. 'Haven't I told you, Grandmother, I won't be treated as an invalid!

Which is one thing I'm certainly not! What is this news? Don't tell me Kalnos has been swept into the sea?'

'No,' the old lady's tone became almost as harsh as his, 'but Panayiotis and Gina Mylonas have been.' She watched Stein closely as his face went blank. 'I'm sorry to have to be the bearer of bad news, Stein. It happened not long after you came here. They were out on the sea at night. A sudden squall, I believe, was responsible. These can happen often, as you know, on such a rock bound coast, and in their flimsy coracle they would stand little chance. Their bodies were found next day.'

'My God!' Stein rose abruptly from the table and Sandra, too, jumped to her feet, wondering how best to comfort him. She wasn't sure how deeply he was shocked, but she recalled him telling her of these people, how well they had looked after him when he was on Kalnos, the care they took of his house when he was not there. Blinded the way he was, all familiar things were doubly precious and this tragic news must indeed be a blow.

He walked to the window, standing against the darkness of the glass, his tall, well muscled figure giving the impression of indomitable strength and Sandra wasn't sure how to approach him. He raised, as usual, an impregnable barricade between himself and sympathy. Silently the two women watched him, united, at least on this occasion, by their deep concern for him, but when at last he returned to the table his face was once again impassive.

Madame waited a moment until he was seated, then resumed her argument. 'So you see, Stein, it is not possible for you and Sandra to go there alone without servants. That she is your fiancée only makes the situation more difficult, and to take friends as chaperones would mean you would not be any better off than you are here.'

'There is one way,' he smiled thinly as he looked at Sandra, and she shuddered, seeming to find a hint of the diabolical in the smile that glinted on his hard features.

What awful plan was he hatching up? As long as it didn't concern her she didn't mind!

'Sandra,' he continued, without further explanation to his grandmother, 'you wanted a word with me and, as I must certainly have one with you, I suggest we walk in the gardens. When we come back we might be able to discuss the future more clearly.'

As Sandra, with a murmur of apology to Madame Kartalis, followed him to the garden, her pulse beating heavily with nervous agitation, something told her she wasn't going to hear anything she would welcome. Away from the house she thought she might feel better, but curiously did not. Stein took her arm, but it was he who did the guiding, which proved how familiar he was in these surroundings. They walked to the pool in the moonlight through air which was fragrant with the scent of flowers.

'Stein,' she began hastily, as they traversed a flagged path between a high hedge of cypress, 'I'm sorry about your servants but, as Madame remarked, this seems to make it much more sensible to stay here. Or we could even return to London. I could get a room and help you each day. Or,' she faltered, 'you could find some really expert help. I'm sure there must be plenty available and you would soon get used to someone else.'

'Sit down, Sandra!' They had reached a white-painted bench and he pulled her swiftly to it, sitting himself beside her and keeping hold of her hand. 'Don't worry,' he laughed harshly, 'I don't intend making love to you. I just want to assure myself you will remain until I finish. You have an unfortunate habit of quietly disappearing.'

'What is it you want which seems so important?' she breathed, trying to fix her gaze on the moon rather than him. Annoyingly her voice trembled.

'So you are nervous of me?'

'Sometimes,' she defended herself. 'Your tongue is sharp, *kyrie*.'

This seemed to amuse him slightly, but when she asked quickly if their expedition into the gardens had anything to do with Kalnos at all, he sobered instantly.

'However did you guess?' he mocked.

'It wasn't difficult. Naturally, now your servants are lost we can't go there.'

'Well, I'm certainly not staying here or returning to London.'

Sandra hated his deviousness to the point of exasperation. 'So you do intend going to Kalnos! I expect you can easily find other servants.'

He looked down at her. 'That is the big snag, Sandra, one which my dear grandmother is too aware of. Perhaps I should explain that Kalnos came to me through my mother. It was left to her by her father, my grandfather. I love this part of the world, although normally I don't spend much time in it, but I do find I can work here, especially on Kalnos. Whenever something hasn't worked out the island has always solved my problems.'

'Then,' Sandra forced herself to speak brightly as he paused, 'as I've just said, you must find someone new to look after you.'

Ruefully Stein shrugged. 'This is the snag. The islanders are very superstitious—remember, Kalnos is a very isolated community. For several months they will in some way connect the deaths of Panayiotis and Gina with my house there, rather than the fishing they were doing when they were supposed to be working for me. I may be able to persuade someone that my castle isn't haunted by nereids who lure the innocent inhabitants to their doom, but I doubt it. Meanwhile I am not capable of living there alone.'

'So?'

'So you must come with me, girl. As my wife.'

'As your wife!' Sandra's voice rose, almost croaking with astonishment, yet she couldn't immediately take him seriously. 'You must be joking!'

'No,' he snapped shortly, restraining her as she made to jump up. 'Does the thought alarm you?'

Now she really did feel shocked and her eyes widened, but his face, etched darkly against the moonlight, did nothing to reassure her. He looked deadly serious. 'Stein,' she gasped, 'you promised to set me free after spending a few weeks here. We've been here almost five and I thought you'd be letting me go, but now you're practically ordering me to marry you. Are you crazy?'

'Possibly,' his mouth twisted sardonically. 'I might agree with everything you say, but circumstances have altered in a way I couldn't possibly have foreseen. When you agreed to be my fiancée you also promised to help me with my work, but we haven't done any yet. It's imperative you come with me to Kalnos, and I'm asking you to marry me merely to assure my grandmother's peace of mind. She would feel, if we lived there together unmarried, that we had brought shame on her. Here, you see, etiquette is much stricter than at home. In country districts it is sometimes not even considered proper for a man and a woman to be seen out on their own unless they are engaged.'

'But marriage!' Sandra felt shaken, as if she had been running a long way. How could Stein sit there and discuss such a thing so coolly? She couldn't even think of it like that. Desperately she stared at him. 'Stein, I still think you're crazy. Our contract, if you can call it that, was for just a few weeks; marriage is permanent! Suppose it's simply a business arrangement to satisfy Madame Kartalis, what happens when we return to England?'

'We can get an annulment. There's always divorce.'

The easy way out, or was it? Sandra gazed blankly over the shimmering pool which stretched before them, glinting in the moonlight. When Stein liked he could be extremely glib. He wouldn't think twice of using her, then casting her off, not caring how she suffered. There might be worse fates, but she couldn't think of any. To be made to endure a make-believe engagement was bad enough, but a bogus marriage was surely more than any girl could be expected to tolerate.

'I couldn't,' she whispered fervently, 'I simply couldn't!'

'I'm afraid you'll have to,' he rejoined grimly. 'Nor can I afford to waste time persuading you. I have a contract for my next book and a deadline to meet. I have to go to Kalnos. In fact I need to.'

She felt too stunned to ask what he meant by that and all her resources concentrated on her own predicament. 'You can't force me.'

'Maybe not,' his jaw set harshly, 'but I can make things very difficult for both you and your cousin—if you continue to refuse.'

'Alexandra?'

'The same. Perhaps her new husband would enjoy hearing a few of the more sordid details of her life. I could almost guarantee they would wreck her marriage—but you could always be around to help pick up the pieces.'

'You're despicable!' Sandra gulped, having no idea what he was talking about. 'Have you forgotten you were engaged to her yourself?'

He stared at her, his dark brows narrowing, as if he was undecided about something. 'That's neither here nor there —perhaps I've had a lucky escape. Listen, Sandra,' he relented suddenly, his voice softer, 'I'm merely making a business proposition and you have no need to fear I will take advantage of it.'

Her cheeks hot, she looked at him scornfully. 'I wouldn't let you! But I've read about this kind of thing. I know what can happen eventually. Oh, I know it can end very happily in books, but I don't believe it's at all like that in real life. You're blind,' she rushed on, heedless for once of hurting him, 'you haven't ever seen me. Imagine regaining your sight and seeing what a plain Jane you're married to!'

If she had hoped this would dismay him she was mistaken. 'I don't believe for one minute,' his voice was laced with a faint amusement, 'that you are plain. I've held you, remember, and I can see very clearly with my hands. While you might not be an outstanding beauty, you are slim and your features are regular. I certainly wouldn't anticipate dying with horror if, as you so sweetly put it, I regained my sight.'

Inspiration suddenly shot through Sandra, though it only came reluctantly to her lips. 'What about Sophy?'

'If you mean why don't I ask her to go with me, then forget it. I've already told you this is a business proposition. Sophy is perhaps for the future. I wouldn't insult her with this. She would most likely die of boredom within a week if I took her to Kalnos.'

'And it doesn't matter about me?'

He ignored her bitterness. 'You might not feel so good about this, Sandra, but I can assure you you won't regret it. For a start you can tear up the cheque Arnold gave you. I'll see you're much more satisfied with mine. Don't you think it will be nice to be independent of Alexandra after the way she has treated you? And, as for taking advantage of the situation, when we marry, you can forget that too. Do you think I'd ever want to be permanently committed to someone even distantly connected with my ex-fiancée? When I contemplate a real marriage and family I don't want my son's blood tainted by any similar to hers.'

It was only a week, though it seemed much longer than that, before Sandra sat beside Stein in the hired helicopter on their way to Kalnos. This was the only form of air transport able to land on the island and a stranger flew them. Madame Kartalis had told her Stein was himself an experienced pilot and used to hire a self-drive helicopter in the days before his accident. Sandra could see he didn't care to be just a passenger, but had resigned himself grimly.

Glancing quickly at him now, she drew a quick breath

and looked down at her hands. She and Stein had been married that morning by an obliging *pappas*—priest—on Corfu and the whole ceremony, like the last few days, had seemed slightly unreal. She had worn a calf-length dress in white chiffon with a small white veil. She didn't think she would have bothered, but Madame Kartalis had insisted she be dressed like a proper bride. And, because the old lady was so patently disappointed in Stein's choice of a bride, Sandra had felt, ironically, that she couldn't refuse.

Stein had kept to his expressed intention of buying her a new wardrobe, but she had managed to scrape enough together to buy her own wedding dress. She had been as stubborn over this as Madame had been over the colour. Her old clothes she had given to Katrina, who had been delighted with them, as Stein predicted, but the one new dress she really treasured was her wedding one. She had a curious feeling she would never have another. She loved Stein too much ever to want to marry anyone else. This was the real reason why she had married him.

After their fierce argument in the garden she had vowed never to do as he asked, but next morning she had given in. The thought of him going to Kalnos alone with no one to look after him was more than she could bear. Yet the deep compassion, which seemed to be eating away at her very soul had been nothing to the depth of love she felt for him, a love that seemed to have stirred and blossomed from the very beginning. This morning in the church, as she had walked towards him, she had felt it illuminate her face, to such a degree that she had been shamefully glad he couldn't see. Madame Kartalis, she knew, had, as her sharp old eyes missed very little, but Sandra doubted if this altered the old lady's initial opinion of her.

The ceremony itself had been rather strange, but she had found it immeasurably moving. Stein had complied with a few of the age-old customs by the exchanging of rings and walking three times around the altar. The atmosphere in the small, whitewashed church had been such that it had all seemed completely natural. Surprisingly he had given Sandra another engagement ring, replacing the one she had worn since leaving London. It wasn't as valuable as Alexandra's had been, he warned, but he thought more of it as it had belonged to his mother. Nevertheless, it was a charming ring and, in Sandra's eyes far outshone the more expensive band of pure gold that went on after it.

Afterwards, at the house, there had only been a small reception as Stein had stubbornly held out against inviting everyone they knew. 'Maybe next time,' he had smiled grimly, when his grandmother protested, and only Sandra seemed aware that he meant exactly what he said.

Unconsciously her former fears that he would demand everything a new husband was entitled to began to fade as they flew over the blue Aegean. Below them small islands rose out of the sea, some jet black with volcanic ash but most of them a beautiful verdant green. Sandra was astonished at the number of them. Obligingly the pilot named a few over which they passed and Stein mentioned the occasional one as belonging to a millionaire, some of whom spent almost the entire summer here. From the size of many of the yachts lying at anchorage in the deep, still waters, she was not so surprised to learn of their wealthy owners and felt a very human twinge of envy at the thought of long, sun-baked days on such wonderful shores.

She wasn't sure why she ever imagined it would be, but Kalnos was far from disappointing when they reached it. And because it looked as if it could take some getting around on foot, she was pleased she had a good view of it from the air. It would help her fix a true picture in her mind which might have been impossible otherwise. It was a long island, compared with some—she guessed about four or five English miles, and varied in width. She saw what seemed to be a village about half way along, clinging to a hillside, but most of it looked barren, covered with low

scrub and olive groves. She felt extraordinarily relieved that
the end they were making for seemed wooded, with green
valleys and some mountainous hills; she could even make
out the odd stream tumbling down over rocks.

Over the top of the highest peak the pilot began his
descent and she noticed a house of vast proportions nestling
at the foot of an incline. There didn't appear to be any
proper garden or lawn to land on but, a little distance from
the house, there was a flat paved area and the pilot brought
the helicopter neatly down on this.

'I had this laid out when I used to ferry myself,' Stein
said wryly, indicating the half covered shed at the bottom
of the concrete. 'That was necessary because of the storms
we can get in winter.'

'Oh, I see.' They were standing alone as the pilot had
gone, after declining Stein's offer of a meal. Sandra felt hot
with confusion as the expression on the man's face had
clearly betrayed his feelings. He had obviously decided she
and Stein couldn't wait to get into each other's arms, and
had no wish to witness any embarrassing display of affection.

He need not have worried. Sandra thought it improbable,
even if Stein had been in love, that he would ever show his
feelings in public. Watching him as she stood on the edge
of the terrace, letting the wind play softly over his face, she
was almost envious of his fortitude. What wouldn't she
give for less than half of it!

As if suddenly conscious of her silent regard, he turned
back to her with a rueful sigh. 'Well, here we are, Mrs Freeman. I suppose we'd better get up to the house.'

There was no warmth in his voice to give that derisive
'Mrs Freeman' any special meaning. Sandra shrank.

'You'd better go along, Stein. I'll carry as much as I can.
It's not far.' Her glance went over their few pieces of
luggage.

'Don't be foolish,' his face hardened, 'I didn't marry you

for a slave. Give me your large case and leave the rest. I'll send someone for it.'

'Someone?' She paused as if struck. 'But you said there wouldn't be a servant.'

'There may not be. I don't make any promises,' he retorted impatiently, 'I'm simply hoping. Good wages don't count much with these people, but the fact that I'm blind just might. Also, one of them might feel that such a charming young bride should not be left entirely at the mercy of a husband whose affliction could drive him to harshness.'

She stared. 'Stein——'

He laughed, though she was sure there was little mirth in it. 'I only tease, child. Don't take everything so seriously —that way you invite the devil in me. I ought to have said curiosity might bring our errant islanders when all else fails. These people are romantics. It will intrigue them that their master has brought himself such a beautiful young bride.'

Dismayed, she stared up at him, seeing his dark face, all planes and angles, forgetting how they stood exposed, high up on the naked plateau. 'Please, Stein,' she begged, 'I think I'd much rather manage alone. I—we don't want their curiosity. They'll only wonder and watch.'

'And the morning might bring conclusions you don't like, or should I say ones you won't be over-proud of.'

'I didn't mean——'

'Oh yes, you did,' his eyes glinted coldly. 'In the old days, on these islands, a bride hung the sheet out of the window, come the morning. These people are, in the main, still pagan. You may not believe it, my dear, but they still cling to the old habits.'

Her face scorching, Sandra twisted away from him, her heart thumping. 'Hadn't you better explain, then, that in our case they'll be wasting their time? I don't care what they think, but I won't be watched like a puppet show. Nor do I intend to be!'

With a swift stride he reached her, impaling her against him, 'Nor,' he grated tersely, 'do I intend cooking my own dinner or breakfast. Not if I can help it.'

With quick savagery he lowered his head and she was lost under the dark passion of his kiss. More than that, she felt the old excitement stirring, felt the thrill, at once piercing and sweet, shiver through her entire being. It was a kiss that deepened meaningfully, intensifying desire until her arms went instinctively around his neck so that, outlined against the sunset and a fiery red sky, their bodies appeared to become as one.

Seconds later she was free of his demanding lips and arms as a youth walked towards them across the compound. With his extraordinary sense of perception, Stein must have heard him, but to Sandra the only sound had been the dizzying ring in her ears.

The man—Sandra saw he wasn't so youthful as he drew nearer—was very polite. He obviously knew Stein and murmured a few words of greetings. He then spoke quickly and when Stein nodded his head and said, '*Ne*,' turned to Sandra, waiting to be introduced.

'This is Panos,' Stein explained, as Sandra held out her hand. She had been in Greece long enough to know the Greeks considered this a necessary politeness. '*Kalispera*,' she said.

'Good evening,' Panos replied, in good English.

'Madame doesn't yet speak Greek,' Stein said laconically, 'but she will soon learn. Already,' he cast her a mocking glance, 'she tries.'

Sandra gave a little start, as if realising for the first time her new status as a married woman. She was Madame now, and for reasons of his own Stein seemed to be reminding her of it. Her pale cheeks flushing again she looked inquiringly towards Panos.

'Panos is going to help us,' Stein continued. 'He and his mother will come first thing in the morning. Thyra would have come this evening, but one of her daughter's children is unwell.'

'Oh, I see. How unfortunate!' Anger curling swiftly within her, Sandra forced a sympathetic smile. She couldn't believe it was only her presence that had precipitated such a positive rush of assistance.

As Panos picked up their luggage she hissed, 'This rather contradicts what you told me, Stein!'

'Not necessarily.' He flung her an exasperated glance. 'Alone, I might very easily have stayed that way. They have only come to see the charming young madame. The people of Greece, Sandra, have a great admiration for courage, and here they will consider you have more than enough in marrying a man who can't see.'

'Oh, Stein!' Her voice broke as she tried to stifle her heartache.

'Shut up, my dear.' His civility was curt. 'You must know by now that I prefer other things to pity.'

The house was even larger than the villa in Corfu and she remembered he had called it a castle. It was very like one with its high stone walls and rambling dimensions, but the living quarters were surprisingly modern. It felt, inside, as if the spring sunshine had already warmed it. She was pleasantly surprised. Still shaken from his searching kisses, she felt somehow comforted.

'Shall I take your bags upstairs, *kyrie*?' Panos asked politely.

'Yes, put them in the large room at the end of the corridor,' Stein answered abstractedly.

Minutes later when Panos came down again he said, 'Thank your mother, Panos, tell her we look forward to seeing her in the morning.'

'Yes, *kyrie*.'

Anxiously Sandra watched Panos departing. She removed her coat, without thinking, then wished she hadn't as there seemed nowhere to put it. She would like to have gone upstairs, but felt choked with reluctance to ask Stein where she was to sleep. It was, after all, her wedding day and whether it was a sham or not, she had had enough of his taunting. If she asked about her bedroom she might only be inviting more. The situation reminded her of Athens.

Apparently in no hurry to enlighten her about what was so obviously on her mind, he drawled, 'I'm afraid you'll have to cook our dinner this evening, otherwise we'll have to go hungry. Mind you, I'd be the first to admit it's not the usual thing for a man to ask his bride of only a few hours.'

'Oh, don't be so—so—oh, I don't know what!' Warm with confusion, Sandra flung out her hands helplessly. 'You know ours is just a marriage of convenience!'

'Maybe,' he grunted non-committally. 'All the same, a bride is a bride, whatever the circumstances, and I won't forget it.' He hesitated, turning his head thoughtfully in the direction of the stairs. 'How would you like to shower and get into something less restrictive than I imagine you're wearing? Then we can go to the kitchen and see what there is, perhaps have a picnic in the lounge. If I know anything of Thyra I guess we'll soon be eating more than we need.'

A huge staircase rose darkly from the well of the hall and, as she followed Stein up it, Sandra wondered why she should feel so nervous. It was probably that nothing felt real? She was here in this huge house; she was married but couldn't believe it. Or was it that she didn't want to? If only Stein had loved her—but it grew more apparent he did not. At the same time it also seemed clear he didn't find her altogether repulsive, and men were promiscuous creatures, unlike most women. If the mood took him he might not care whether he loved her or not. Perhaps it was up to her to keep some distance between them and not allow herself to be dominated as he chose.

At the top of the stairs he walked along the twisting corridor with a confidence which again seemed to belie his story that he wasn't too familiar with his island home. He paused exactly beside a heavy oak door. 'I think you'd be wise to take this room next to mine.' Sarcastically he added, 'If you really think you're in any danger you can have one at the other end of the passage or even on the next floor, but in a house this size you might be happier knowing I'm near.'

There seemed sense in this which she couldn't deny or refuse. She decided his offer was a good one, even if not altogether prompted from kindness. Recalling the feeling of warmth she had felt when she first entered, she was sure this wasn't a house to make the flesh creep, but the dark hours of the night might be an entirely different matter.

Stein interpreted her slight silence quite differently. 'Are you still afraid I might ravish you?' he asked curtly.

'No——' she felt so muddled, so torn with strange emotions, she flinched, attempting to squash the wholly irrational suggestion that this might not be too awful. Stein was an extremely attractive man, tall and virile—and her husband. And between them, there was something, she would be the last to say otherwise. But not without love! She could be crying for the moon, but for her any closer relationship would be impossible without that.

Then suddenly, as she glanced at him despairingly, she saw how strained he looked. There was a whiteness beneath his skin and his mouth was held harshly. 'Stein,' she begged, momentarily forgetting herself completely as a strange tenderness swept over her for this man who never seemed to bow down before any infirmity, 'Stein, I don't really mind where I sleep. I trust you.' As if to emphasise this she laid a tentative hand on his arm.

In hoping to say the right thing she failed miserably. His eyes hardened. 'You believe in tying a man's hands, don't you, Sandra? You declare you trust me, hoping such an innocent statement will keep me at bay. It was never prompted from that frozen little heart of yours, only from a sense of self-preservation.'

'Please, Stein . . .'

'Don't plead with me!' He brushed her hand away contemptuously. 'I wonder how you will react when, one day, I might not need your pity any more? Don't try me too far, my dear. Don't forget I am half Greek and was brought up to think wholly as one, to act as they do on these islands. Here I was taught that a woman is merely subservient. If I were to make proper love to you, here and now, until you perhaps screamed for mercy, I would only gain status.' With uncanny accuracy he paused to grasp her thin shoulders oppressively. 'And don't tell me you wouldn't enjoy it. Even without seeing you I am well aware how you are fashioned, how you are capable of a depth of response which might completely shake you.'

Before she could gasp a reply, if indeed she had been capable of it, he released her as suddenly as he had taken her. With a half smothered exclamation he left her to enter his bedroom, slamming the door. Again she was forcibly reminded of the hotel in Athens and shrank from his continuing derision. Dear God, if only she could be back in England with Gran—but Gran wasn't there any more and it was senseless to long feverishly for the comfort of her usually sound advice. Gran, in a way, had been like Madame Kartalis, outspoken, not above being waspish, but so full of common sense that Sandra didn't know how she could ever hope to manage properly without her.

Hopelessly Sandra turned and opened her own bedroom door. What was the use of a lot of stupid wishing and weeping for the past? It was the present she must concern herself with, this strange marriage, her new husband. Whatever she said or did seemed to be wrong. With Stein it was rather like finding one's way through a trackless jungle. He could be easy, almost tender, or suddenly just the opposite, whichever way his changing moods took him. If she couldn't judge beforehand how he was going to react to what she said then she could be going to suffer. Somehow she must learn to think carefully, and this could be difficult as often, she realised, she spoke too impulsively.

Trying to blot from her mind his terse summing up of her emotional possibilities, she explored her bedroom, finding it much as she expected. The furniture was heavy, dark with age but, like the floor, polished to a beautiful burnished gloss. The bed was large, too, its spotless linen giving an air of luxurious comfort. Only the leopard skins flung over the foot of it made her shiver. In the adjoining bathroom the impression of luxury was continued.

Someone had spent money here. Sandra had no doubt her stay would be a comfortable one, but she felt bewildered as she gazed around. If only she could forget tonight was her wedding night she might even sleep well. She didn't think Stein would break his word. Not that he had promised anything, exactly, apart from making it clear that he was only interested in her ability to help him with his work, but she envied him his ability to dissociate himself from anything else. It was no use her wishing secretly and shamefully that she could be in his arms. Hastily, as she slipped out of her shoes, she corrected herself. She didn't want to be there, not really, but it would have been nice to be held and comforted. Comforted against what? Sandra wasn't sure how to answer such a confusing query. Nor did she stop to ask herself if this was entirely what a new bridegroom might be expected to have in mind.

# CHAPTER SEVEN

A WEEK later Sandra was still beset by longings, but these were nowhere near as vague as they had been that first night. So far as work went nothing could have gone better, with Stein soon getting the hang of dictating and her typing improving daily to speeds which earned his approval. It was the sudden flares of tension between them that kept her strung up to a pitch where she dared not let herself relax, for fear she should find herself overwhelmed by the sometimes urgent desire to touch him. This, she knew, would never do. If he demanded an explanation she wouldn't know what to say for herself.

On Corfu there had been other people, but here they were very much alone. Panos and his mother came every day, but they didn't stay during the night, and the nights were the worst. The long, lonely hours when Sandra failed to sleep, when her body seemed plagued by an unremitting restlessness which often caused her to leave her bed and steal downstairs into the vast kitchen below to seek a hot drink in the vain hope of subduing the inexplicable turmoil in her mind and body.

She was thankful the house wasn't too dark at night. Stein, years ago, had installed a powerful generator, capable of throwing light into the darkest corner. It ran, along with other things, a huge deep freeze that he arranged to have replenished whenever he intended spending some time on the island. On the first evening she had been quite startled. Having expected to concoct a meal from a few basic local ingredients, when he had shown her what was actually available, she had almost gasped.

Being usually just a passable cook she had been secretly

114

rather proud of the meal she had produced that night. The steak, perhaps because she had prayed so hard, had been done to a turn, so had the frozen chips and peas.

'We could well be back home,' she had said, watching him carefully as he ate with apparent contentment.

'Yes,' he cynically agreed, 'if you're talking of the food, but don't forget my palate is more cosmopolitan than yours. Still, it's always nice to return to the normally plain fare of dear old England.'

After that she hadn't felt quite so proud of herself, but there had been no sense of alarm until a moment later when she'd noticed the hard set of his mouth. When he had gone on to ask, with what seemed deliberate emphasis, if this was all she had to offer, she fancied she had known exactly what he meant.

Either way the answer had to be yes. If he had loved her, been tender, instead of sitting there so tall, and darkly forbidding, she might have responded to his derisive joke differently.

'Perhaps,' he rasped, 'you should concentrate on Greek cookery for a change. You'll find it has a distinct flavour. Indirectly it might even help you to understand me better. I suspect you continue to associate me with the more intrepid Englishmen you've known. You must get used to the idea that I'm not like this, not underneath.'

Hastily Sandra had gulped. 'There seems little sense in getting to know each other better, does there? Not in our kind of marriage.'

'No?' His hand shot out to cover hers, catching her nervous tremor. 'I think it's a little too early to come to any definite conclusions about what kind of marriage we have. A man might have second thoughts about anything. See how you tremble. Don't tell me you don't know what I'm talking about?'

'I think you're being unfair,' her voice came low.

'Not really,' he had drawled, removing his hand with a

shrug. 'I'm simply warning you not to drive me too far. Otherwise I can't be responsible for the mixed blood in my veins.'

They had wine that night and every night since. Stein disappeared before dinner into the spacious cellars below the kitchens and returned with cobweb-covered bottles, the labels of which he ordered Sandra to read out to him.

'I'm quite used to negotiating the cellar steps in the dark, but I'm afraid I can't remember where to find each bottle.'

He had drunk the wine morosely and, refusing coffee, said quite calmly that Sandra had better go to bed. It was late, she must be tired. He was going to listen to a little music and would be up later.

Sandra hesitated, aware that she would rather have joined him and feeling curiously reluctant to do as he suggested. Unreasonably, her cheeks hot, she was conscious of feeling cheated. It might, at least, have given her something pleasant to remember of her wedding day, to have been able to sit and relax with him for an hour instead of being sent, like a small child, to bed. It would have made the pretty dress she wore, the effort she had made to look nice, not seem wasted. But another glance at his set face had knocked such a notion apprehensively from her head and sent her scuttling ignominiously upstairs.

In the morning she had met Panos's mother, Thyra, who like her son spoke fairly good English. Sandra liked her immediately, although Stein had mentioned that she wasn't as expert as his last servants had been and that she would have to make allowances. They had been lucky to get anybody.

Because she fancied he sounded patronising, she retorted sharply, 'I'm not used to being waited on hand and foot! Before Gran died we didn't have any help whatsoever. I did everything.'

'And you consider that a virtue?' he had sneered, unimpressed. 'Well, you won't have to soil your white hands again, not that way. There might be problems here, I'm not altogether sure that Thyra will prove satisfactory, but in England I will supply all the fully trained help you need.'

Love in a cottage, Sandra thought wistfully, was not something Stein considered. And he seemed to be constantly forgetting that theirs was not meant to be a permanent relationship, while she grew tired of reminding him. When she did it only gave him the opportunity to declare that he could discard her whenever it suited him.

'Thyra and I will get on very well,' she assured him stiffly, declining to make any comment on her future position in England. Thyra looked a kindly woman and had given Sandra no reason to think she disapproved of her not being a real wife. The things Stein had said about a normal Greek wedding night faded uneasily from her mind. Thyra clearly didn't believe it was any of her business. Or was it, perhaps, that she was too absorbed in the problems of her own family to worry about those of another?

There was no pool here, so they bathed in the sea. Stein had found her down on the beach, early on the morning of their second day. The hot drink she had indulged in the night before hadn't seemed to work, and rather than lie awake any longer she had got up and come down here. Idly she had been standing watching the blue Aegean lap the white sands, wondering carelessly if there were any unknown hazards. The air was beautiful, mild and warm with no wind, the promise of summer everywhere. Everything within her began to respond, she felt herself slowly relax as the confusing tensions of the night fell away from her.

Not hearing Stein approach, she was startled as she swung around. He wore only the briefest of trunks, they looked as if they had been dug out for her benefit, something he had once worn when he was much younger and slimmer. They fitted closely around his now very masculine hips and she felt her eyes wandering widely over his lightly tanned body.

It was apparent he intended to swim. 'Oh, Stein,' she breathed, suddenly worried out of her guilty absorption as he paused beside her, 'you can't be thinking of going in?'

'Why not?' His mouth curled with such derisive amusement she was glad he couldn't see her pale cheeks.

'There must be danger for—for someone like you,' she insisted bravely. 'I heard someone on Corfu talking of sharks.'

'You're much too susceptible to rumour,' he quipped. 'Of course there are hazards everywhere in the world. If we stopped to think of them all we'd never get anywhere. I used to swim very frequently at night when the only light was the merest touch of phosphorescence. This is best seen on moonlight nights in late August and September, but often I've known every ripple outlined with darting sparkles of greenish fire. Occasionally I seemed to be lost in the middle of countless millions of green sparks, like a baptism of variegated fireworks.'

'Don't they burn?'

'No, of course not,' his mouth softened, as it sometimes did when he talked of the past or was more tolerant of her young uncertainty, 'but they can give that impression. In fact the sensation can be extremely convincing, so that on bad nights one doesn't usually loiter. Naturally there's never any actual fire, that's only in the imagination. Certainly one couldn't be hurt by it and this phosphorescent sea is well worth seeing.'

'I don't suppose we'll be here at that time of the year,' she said wistfully, 'unless you haven't finished your book.'

'We may have to return to England before that,' he replied. Then, without giving her a chance to ask why, he had exclaimed, 'Aren't you coming in?'

She had gone swimming with him because it had seemed foolish not to. Apart from that she couldn't bear to think of him, perhaps in difficulties, out there alone. She was a good swimmer, thanks to expert tuition at school and, afterwards, the local baths, and she managed to stay at Stein's side, although she suspected he regulated his more powerful strokes to comply with hers.

The water was warm but buoyant and she enjoyed that first swim immensely, and was thrilled by Stein's smile of approval when they reached the shore again.

'You're good. When a girl of your age swims as you do it usually means she's interested.'

'Yes, I am,' she replied eagerly, managing to pass him his towel without looking at him too directly. The sight of his strong, lean body dripping with water seemed to do strange things to her pulse. Without thinking, she added, 'I should like to try surfing.'

'Sorry,' he froze back to his usual hardness, 'that's out for me at the moment and I couldn't allow you to go alone, not as a learner. Nor do I want you asking Panos to teach you. He's something of an expert, but over-fond of taking risks—risks I don't particularly want my wife running.'

'Oh—it's me who should be sorry for suggesting it.' She had been stricken with remorse for blundering so. It shouldn't be so difficult to remember all the things Stein could no longer do!

'Forget it,' he'd said curtly. 'You can't help being a stupid little fool. Just keep it in your head that I won't allow surfing.'

Stung by his disparagement, she retorted sharply, 'The list of things you won't allow grows daily, and to an amazing length, considering ours is not a real marriage.'

'Whose fault is that?' He scrubbed his towel harshly over broad shoulders. 'Yours and your despicable cousin's, if you're looking for names.'

'You can't forget, can you!'

Suddenly they were quarrelling fiercely, her voice unsteady but determined, his insultingly vindictive. 'I'm wiser not to.'

Sandra clutched her own towel to her skimpy bikini protectively. 'I don't think you'd have been happy with Alexandra, and I believe you know it. These last few days——'

Suddenly, to her despair, he grabbed her, his hands clamping her bare shoulders like a kind of punishment. 'Yes? I'd be interested to know what conclusions you've come to about these last few days. Don't stop there.'

'None!' She'd tried to wriggle free, but when she didn't succeed, she stopped struggling. This, she had learnt, only incited him. He hadn't directly answered her question, but she might as well answer his. 'You don't act like a man in the throes of unrequited love!'

'Dear me,' he jibed, 'you sound like a lost line out of Shakespeare. Maybe you think I'm more bent on avenging a new one?'

Bitterly she agreed, 'It's more than likely you're subconsciously seeking revenge on me, but you shouldn't lay the whole blame on my shoulders. Your own actions, as much as anything else, must be keeping you from your true love.'

His voice became icy. 'What a glib little tongue you have! So you believe that in marrying you I've inadvertently sacrificed the hope of marrying anyone else. But haven't you just said ours is not a real marriage? You forget I arranged it for convenience, not love, and that it's soon to be dissolved.'

'You don't consider anyone but yourself, do you?' She recalled Sophy's angry face at their wedding with regret. 'I'm sure Sophy doesn't appreciate your devious tactics.'

'No one appears to, so why should I worry about any one of you?' he ground out. His face darkened as he slid firm hands down her damp arms, ignoring her reference to Sophy. 'Maybe I shouldn't try to be so stringent with myself. Why shouldn't I indulge myself for a change? Your opinion of me, it seems, couldn't be worse.'

He had kissed her then, much to her angry surprise, in a manner she found humiliating but exciting. It was like being exposed to a positive avalanche of indescribable feelings, yet all over so quickly there was no time to explore any one of them. On regaining her senses she had found herself standing inches away from him, only his harsh voice taunting her.

'You're like strong wine, girl. You could go to my head if I had too much of you, and that could only lead to complications.'

Now, remembering, Sandra turned restlessly in her bed. It had happened four days ago, but try as she might she couldn't forget it, just as she seemed unable to put from her mind anything that had taken place between them since. Stein's ambiguous remarks were the worst to put up with but, if it was any consolation, work-wise she seemed to satisfy him.

Unhappily she turned over yet again, grabbing impatiently at a sliding sheet, wondering just where this strange marriage might take her. Stein was only beginning the third chapter of his book, they could be here a long time, for all he said otherwise. Somehow she wasn't sure she could stand it.

She must have dropped off and, like most sudden awakenings, was not sure what had aroused her. There was nothing disturbing, the silence and darkness not being eerie, so she couldn't think what could have been responsible. Perhaps her imagination? It was then she heard the muffled groans coming through the wall from Stein's room, of his voice raised in deep agony before subsiding again, and the sound of a heavy object crashing to the floor. Her immediate impression was that he was being attacked, her one thought to dash to his assistance. How could he help himself if he couldn't see! In a second she was out of bed and, without waiting to find her wrap, fled out of her room into his.

As the door gave under her urgent fingers she could hear him muttering harshly but, to her startled amazement, there was no one in the room but himself. The moonlight, coming in through the uncurtained window, would have shown an intruder clearly. It was obvious Stein was having some kind of nightmare, from the way in which he tossed about. It was equally obvious, from the way his bedclothes lay in a crumpled heap on the floor, that it had been going on for some time.

Horrified, Sandra watched frozen as, clad only in silk pyjama trousers, he lay on his face pushing with pounding hands at the mattress. Suddenly she could bear it no longer. As if released from paralysis she rushed across to his bed, grasping him by his shoulders, trying, in spite of her half hysterical concern for him, to do so carefully. Hadn't she read somewhere to treat people gently, if possible, in such circumstances?

'Stein darling,' she cried frantically, 'you must stop it! It's Sandra!'

He turned abruptly, knocking her hand away with a force that almost sent her spinning. 'Damn you!' he shouted hoarsely, 'can't you get me out of here?'

'Stein!' Again she tried desperately as it dawned on her that he might imagine himself still in his burning car. 'You're all right, you aren't trapped anywhere. It's only a bad dream!'

At first she thought he didn't hear her. Then his hands came out, catching her as quickly as he had knocked her away. 'Your fault,' he accused thickly, 'you little bitch! I'd like to——'

'Stein!' Despairingly she repeated his name the third time, in her need to get through to him not caring how he hurt her. 'You've got it all wrong, but it doesn't matter, if only you'd wake up!'

Once more she thought she had failed, then his face slowly relaxed and the tension drained from his big body as he regarded her with incredulous stupefaction. It was as if, without sight, he could clearly see the white terror on her face.

'Sandra! What on earth are you doing here?'

She sensed he moderated his language with difficulty, but she didn't miss the disapproving grimness. 'You were having a nightmare, Stein—at least that's what I think it was. I heard you from next door.'

'Where you should have had the sense to stay.' His gratitude wasn't overwhelming.

'How could I?' She didn't try to hide the resentment he so often aroused. 'You were shouting your head off! I wouldn't like to think, had it been me you would simply have turned over and gone to sleep again.'

One of his hands left her to rub over his still perspiring brow. The gesture seemed to make him doubly vulnerable and her heart shook with pity.

'Oh, Stein,' she added impulsively, 'what sort of wife would I be if I'd simply ignored you?'

Swiftly, as his composure returned so did his usual cynicism. 'I didn't think you'd endeavoured to be any kind of proper kind of wife so far. Does this mean you've changed your mind? That you're thinking of becoming a little more amenable?'

'You're changing the subject,' she whispered hoarsely. 'We were talking of you, your nightmare. Do you have it often?'

'Not so often now,' he admitted briefly. 'I still occasionally dream I'm trapped in that damned car, but there's really nothing to worry about. I suppose,' his mouth quirked wryly, 'I should have warned you, though.'

'You could have done. It might have helped—you, I mean, if you'd been able to bring yourself to talk about it.' Sighing, and before quite realising what she was doing, she leant forward, gently brushing a strand of thick dark hair off his forehead. She could feel he was still hot and her previous resentment faded. 'Can I get you a drink, Stein?'

'No,' his voice curiously thickened, 'I haven't that kind of thirst.'

Something about him, as he watched her grimly, unsmiling, should have warned her, but her concern for him was such that she hadn't given her own position much thought. 'Stein,' she muttered, still living his nightmare for him, tears brimming her green eyes, 'I got so worried for you. When I heard you ...' Her voice caught on a sob and she couldn't go on, as his agony seemed to transfer to her very bones.

'Come here, girl.' His words were brief but his growl was warm as his bare arms pulled her to him and a hand stroked down her slender back holding her completely against him. 'It's all right,' his deep voice murmured in her ear, 'I don't want you worried, but I do appreciate that you came.'

Sandra meant to push him away with a small joke, but she felt too choked to utter a word. Instead she found herself clinging to him, drinking in the male scent of his skin, held by the tension which mounted unbearably between them. As his hand soothed away her tears she lifted her head to look at him, seeing his face, drawn darkly against the dim light of the moon. Still half dazed by what had happened, she felt weak, her one inclination to hold on to him yet subtly aware that it wasn't only his sympathy she wanted. Loving him, she was aware of a rush of primitive emotion, while knowing she mustn't give way to it. If he belonged to anyone it was Sophy. She was the one he had been attracted to after Alexandra. Sandra Weir didn't exist except as someone to be made use of!

Making a great effort, she tried to free herself. 'I must go now,' she said bleakly, 'if you're sure you'll be all right.'

'No.'

He wouldn't let her go and she could feel the heavy beat of his heart through the thin silk of her nightgown as he pulled her quickly down to his side on the bed. Because he wore only pyjama trousers his chest was bare and he seemed peculiarly pagan in the moonlight. His eyes, as they looked down on her, contained a curious mixture of anger and tenderness, a dark smouldering she couldn't find strength to resist. With a little moan she buried her face against him again, the heat in her breast spreading to every sensitive part of her body. She couldn't stop herself from touching him, couldn't prevent her arms going around him, feeling beneath her hands the tensed muscles of his back. Clinging to him convulsively, she pressed softly consoling little kisses on his face, on his skin, as if supplicating such silent devotion to renew what was most precious to him—his sight.

Under the feverish pressure of her lips his calm broke, the gentleness in him changing to a sudden urgency as he drew her closer, his fingers threading through her hair as he pulled her head back to the pillow. With a half bitten off exclamation he began moving his lips over hers as he started making love to her. He leant over her, his weight pressing her down, his hands pushing ruthlessly through the fragile silk of her brief attire to find her breasts. There was a hunger in him that wouldn't be denied and he seemed bent on arousing her to the same pitch of desire.

With a soft, inarticulate moan of longing every sensible precaution disappeared from Sandra's mind. They were married, would it be so very dreadful to give in to him, to belong to him completely? Could the outside world matter, need anything else be allowed to? Weren't their immediate feelings, her own and Stein's, all that mattered? Their eagerness to share such passionate delight?

She lay in his arms, whispering his name as his hands and mouth travelled sensuously over her, melting her flesh to her very bones. Never had she known anything remotely like it, never been aware of so much wanton desire. Surely it couldn't be so wrong to feel like this, especially if responding to such feelings brought some light into Stein's dark life?

He held her ever more closely and, as his passion mounted, his mouth came back to cover hers, kissing her with almost unbearable yearning until she trembled uncontrollably from the small flames which ran through her and her arms clung around his neck, her fingers buried fiercely in the crisp dark waves of his hair.

Seconds later she felt stunned when he pushed her from him. After being so carried away it wasn't so easy to come back to earth. 'Stein, is something wrong?' It was all she could do to ask as her voice shook.

'No,' he pulled himself up, thrusting his broad shoulders against the back of the bed, disengaging himself firmly from her clinging arms, 'but there might have been if I hadn't remembered your treachery. If you remained here with me all night, our marriage could never be dissolved.'

Horrified, she stared up at him from where she still lay against his pillows. Sensuous fire still ran through her body but her desire for him had come initially from her heart. Now, as she realised his was only a physical involvement, passion began to die within her, leaving only devastating shame.

'An annulment is important to you?' she whispered.

'For you, too,' he corrected, his face impassive again. 'You wouldn't have thanked me in the morning.'

Her voice was unsteady, much as she tried to control it. 'Don't you mean it the other way round? You can't really wait to be rid of me.'

'I'm certainly not going to put any obstacles in the way,' he agreed harshly. 'If you think I'm going to jeopardise the chance of a sane, woman-free life because I couldn't resist a little bitch who knows how to use her body, then you're mistaken.'

It was as if he had raised a knife and slain her on the spot. Her humiliation deepened, washing over her in great waves. 'I didn't deliberately act like—like that,' she stammered.

'Didn't you?' Just as she was about to flee, his hands were out shaking her, not caring how they hurt. 'Your cousin was cold, but she had contriving wits. With you it's both your body and mind. Don't tell me you've never lain with a man before—you know exactly how to go about it. With every tantalising inch of you, you know how to make a man desire you, so that his common sense soon disappears. Well, thank heavens mine returned in time!'

'You couldn't have been so carried away, then,' she cried, wanting to hurt him as he did her. 'I believe you're just trying to find an excuse for making love to me. You certainly never got that much carried away, since you stopped when you wanted to.'

'Damn you!' he rasped, his next words seeming to be dragged from him reluctantly. 'It was a sudden pain over my eyes.'

'Your eyes!' At once forgetting her anger, she was all concern. Remorse shook her, as it did so often. 'Oh, darling ...'

'Forget it!' Impatiently he shook off her anxious hand. 'Don't pretend to be concerned again. The pain's gone now, but this time I've reason to be grateful it came. You'd better get along to your own bed. I don't want you any longer in mine.'

Nothing could have been much plainer than that! Huddled over a cup of coffee next morning in the kitchen, Sandra reflected wearily while listening with one ear to Thyra's complaints about the lights. The generator was playing up, it seemed. Dinner, last evening, had been all but spoilt.

Dinner wasn't the only thing better forgotten. Sandra's eyes lustreless for want of sleep, regarded the woman's anxious face with apathy. 'I'll mention it to Mr Freeman,' she promised.

'If it breaks down completely, madame, there could be much waste. Apart from the lights and cooking there is the deep freeze. Kyrios Stein used to overhaul it himself before his accident, I believe.'

Sandra frowned. Now he wasn't able to see that even the lights were working properly! 'Is there no one else on the island with the—er—know-how?'

'I beg your pardon, madame?'

'I mean, isn't there anyone who knows about generators? What about Panos?'

'There's no one, madame,' Thyra shook her head. 'This is only a small island, a few fishermen, a few farms. We make enough for a modest living, but·we have no electric light. Kyrios Stein did offer to install it free, but we haven't yet made up our minds.'

'Wouldn't it be useful?' Sandra asked, wanting to talk—anything to keep her mind off the previous night.

'Yes,' Thyra smiled, her pleasant face lighting up, 'we are not a backward people. On the islands, if you sometimes get this impression, it is only because we deliberately cling to the old-fashioned ways. Often we pretend to live more in the past than we actually do as the tourist likes to feel he is in another world. But the average Greek is as shrewd and well informed as anyone else.'

'I never thought otherwise,' Sandra smiled, as indeed she hadn't until meeting Stein's grandmother. It had been she who insisted that the old ways were still very much observed and Stein, strangely enough, who had supported her views. Sandra felt she might have been warned by her own grandmother who, because she had been forty when Sandra's father was born, had seemed quite an old lady to Sandra before she had died. Hadn't Gran spent hours regretting 'the things young people got up to nowadays' and trying to make Sandra live as she had done?

'I'll have a word with my husband,' she promised again, and was rewarded by another grateful smile.

She found him in the room where they usually worked, playing back the work they had done the day before, and he wasn't too tolerant about the generator.

'Every time the wind blows and there's a flicker, Thyra will panic. I'll look at it if I get a minute.'

He was in no mood, she could see, for further discussion on the subject, so she didn't insist he should do something right away. After last night she refused to be anxious that he might try to go out in the dark and put the thing right. That was up to him!

'Are you satisfied with yesterday's effort?' she asked, deliberately infusing into her voice a cool indifference which she sensed would annoy him. Desperately she tried not to take advantage of his blindness by gazing at him, allowing her eyes to eat him up.

'I'm not sure,' for once he didn't seem to notice her tone as his fingers flicked the recorder switch. 'I'm playing it back too soon, but you're late this morning.'

'I'm sorry,' she apologised briefly.

Unprepared for his curtness, she stepped back involuntarily when he spoke. 'Stop acting like a martyr, Sandra. You're not the only one who feels hard done by. In time you'll forget—if you stay out of my bedroom.'

'I'll never go near it again, so you can stop worrying!' she exclaimed vehemently, conscious of a sudden frustrating desire to hit him. He made her sound like a tramp—and feel like one, too!

As if sensing her violent inclinations, he moved his tall body nearer. 'Would once do,' he jeered, 'or would you like to hit me twice? Such a pity I'm a blind man. It would be on your soft little conscience all day, wouldn't it?'

Not surprisingly Sandra lost control, swinging her hand with force. But with the swift intuition that made her so often wonder if he could see a little, his own hand lifted to catch hers.

'If you slap me I'll only slap back,' he grunted. 'Aren't you bruised enough this morning? I seem to recall ...'

Wrenching her arm free, she put the width of the room between them as she cut in, 'How dare you refer to that!'

'It might serve as a warning. In retrospect you might be inclined to regard our little fiasco in a rosier light.' His face hardened. 'Next time you might not get off so lightly.'

Taking a grip of herself, Sandra managed to ignore this, picking up her pad in dignified silence. She knew when she was beaten and there could be little sense in antagonising him completely. Rustling some papers as she searched for a pen seemed to give him some indication that she intended to work.

She watched as he shrugged and walked back to his chair. 'I suppose we may as well make a start.'

'I'm ready when you are,' she agreed coldly, and hated him because of his cynical smile.

They did so much that day that long before evening she felt mentally exhausted. She felt even worse when Stein informed her that he was far from pleased with any of it. He went so far as to say he considered all the hours they had spent a waste of time and put the tape she had just recorded in the fire.

Tears of frustration in her eyes, she watched it burn, but that didn't hurt nearly so much as what came after.

Grimly turning away from the flames, he said, 'I don't think your coming here was such a good idea after all.'

Which seemed to cap her own conclusions that she was an all-round failure. Almost she decided not to come down to dinner. It was only the thought of Thyra being hurt that brought her.

The meal, she felt, was a failure too, with Stein sitting silent throughout and drinking too much. While she tried to convince herself she hated him but was unable to remove her eyes for long from his dark, handsome face. When she asked to be excused soon afterwards he didn't so much as reply.

In her room, with sleeplessness again troubling her, the now established routine of going downstairs to make a cup of tea or coffee had to be gone through. It was while she was coming back, carrying her hot drink, that the lights failed.

Nearly at the top of the stairs she halted abruptly, quite unable to see where she was going. Her attention wholly on the impenetrable darkness, she forgot about the mug she clutched until it fell from her nervous hand with a re-sounding clatter as it bounced down the stone steps before shattering in a thousand pieces at the bottom.

Sandra's sharp cry of dismay was as much of reaction as anything else, and it rose to a terrified scream as every tense nerve in her head seemed to tighten excruciatingly. Her hand groping for the stair-rail encountered nothing, which gave her the odd impression of falling, and she screamed again before collapsing on to the stairs with a low moan. It was a long time since she had felt remotely like this. Not since she had first gone, as a small child, to live at The Elms, and Gran insisted she have no night-light, not even in so large a house. Desperately she tried to re-strain a mounting hysteria. It was no use thinking of that now! It was only the generator which had broken down, there was nothing else to frighten her. Yet somehow the house seemed much more alarming in the dark. Everything creaked, there were sounds everywhere, not least that of the rising wind, shaking the old roof, sending spirals of cold air under the huge doors, up the old staircase to tease her bare feet.

'Sandra—is that you?'

She hadn't heard Stein coming, but the sound of his voice should have brought relief. Instead, jumping up too quickly, she bumped into his hard body and another frantic cry escaped her as she clutched him wildly. 'Stein!'

'Good heavens, girl!' His arms enclosed her tightly, protectively, but like the night before his voice was tinged with impatience. 'whatever is the matter? I heard you scream and you're shaking like a leaf!'

# CHAPTER EIGHT

IT seemed a long time before she could speak coherently, but she knew, it was only seconds. Was this how Stein had felt when he had first been blinded? Every day, every experience like this, brought her fresh understanding.

Yet, as her thoughts softened, his apparently took entirely the opposite direction. 'Sandra—what the hell! Don't you think I had enough last night without a continuation of your little games?'

A great cold encompassed her. So that was what he thought? Numbly she forced unwilling limbs to withdraw from his arms. 'It's the lights.'

'The lights?'

Much as she stiffened he didn't let her go. 'Thyra warned us about the generator.'

'Oh, that!' His terse sigh smote her cheek as he held her. 'I forgot all about it. But what on earth are you doing down here in this state?'

'I wasn't in this state until the lights went,' she quivered resentfully. 'I went down for a drink.'

'Was that it rolling down the stairs?'

'Yes.' Again she tried to ease away from him, aware that the fear which flooded her body was being rapidly replaced by an emotion of another kind, even more devastating.

'You certainly make a din! Your scream could have scared me out of my wits. So you couldn't sleep?'

'I'm sorry if I woke you.'

He neither denied nor confirmed it. 'Darkness doesn't bother me now. I've come to terms with it. That drink—was it hot?'

'Just tea.'

'But did it scald you!'

It seemed crazy to be standing there, talking in low, hurried voices, one against the other, as if each was afraid of pausing for breath. 'No. It only caught my arm. I don't think there's any damage.'

He sounded grim—she didn't know if he looked it. 'Sometimes I'm not sure what I'm going to do with you, Sandra. You run about in the night with practically nothing on, a source of constant disturbance.'

'I'm sorry!' He didn't say whom it was she disturbed but, if it were himself, it could only be in the purely impersonal sense. She would like to have moved completely away from him, but the darkness was such that she might never find him again. Below her the hall yawned like a bottomless pit, above the corridors twisted deviously. 'You don't wear much yourself,' she forced herself to take the offensive.

'I was in bed, remember.' He paused. his chin reflectively scrubbing the top of her head. 'If you're feeling better I'd like to get you some form of temporary light until morning. There's nothing much I can do about the generator until then.'

All the way to the kitchen Stein kept his arm around her and she didn't object, knowing she couldn't have found her way alone. He told her where to find matches, then lamps, but the latter, to her dismay, were empty and there was no kersosene.

'Damn!' Stein frowned, in the glow of the flickering match as, in a cellar, he surveyed the empty drum. 'I should have checked. I should have remembered that Panayiotis, the one who was drowned, used the lamps for his fishing. We had an arrangement and he always kept the tanks well filled.'

'What do we do now?' Sandra enquired, as they made

their way back to the kitchens. 'Not even a candle, and I can't strike matches all night.'

'I'm afraid you'll just have to bear the darkness until it's time to get up,' he drawled. 'I'll get you a brandy as you might still be suffering from shock, but after that you're on your own.'

In the face of such harsh indifference she felt like screaming that he could keep his drink, but common sense prevailed. She might need it if she was to spend the rest of the night alone in that huge bedroom. Not that she ever kept a light on while she slept, but the comfort of knowing it was there prevented her from being afraid.

Feeling an irrational resentment at the way in which he managed in the dark, she swallowed her drink, without apology for choking as it went down.

'Half a glass of that,' Stein quipped dryly, taking the empty tumbler, 'should settle you better than tea.'

'Half a glass! Oh, well, perhaps he was right, but she suspected he was secretly laughing at her. Her legs did feel a little unsteady, but that was only because of her fright. There was still the darkness and loneliness upstairs to be faced.

Near the bottom of the stairs, coming down, she had been glad of the slippers Stein found for her, as a precaution against broken china, but somewhere one had fallen off. Now, as she trod on a sharp fragment, she cried out.

'Now what's wrong!'

'Nothing!' Her voice squeaked as she hopped. 'I've just stepped on something!'

'Where are the slippers I gave you?'

'They—I mean one of them fell off.'

'You shouldn't have such small feet.'

They were at it again, talking quickly, but while Stein's tone was steady and grim, Sandra's shook. 'That doesn't solve my immediate problem.' Bending down, she removed a piece of glass from her foot.

Before she could protest he swung her up in his arms,

lifting her so easily she might have been thistledown. 'God give me patience!' he ground out. 'If I don't do something we'll never get anywhere, and obviously, you'd only lose more slippers.'

Cradled against his broad chest she felt completely safe, never wanting to leave it, although, for appearances' sake, she put up a small struggle.

'Behave yourself, or I'll lock you in the cellar. You're drunk.'

'I'm not!' But instead of taking offence she turned her face into the rough towelling of his robe, which could have been the finest silk, so comforting did it feel against her cheek. It was heaven to be so near him—the truth could no longer be suppressed. If only she could remain here for ever!

She didn't want to be put down but, as if entirely unaware of her thoughts, Stein dropped her gently outside her door.

Shuddering in the opaque blackness around them, she wasn't too proud to keep hold of his arm. 'Stein, I can't stay there by myself. Couldn't we go back down and light a fire?'

He sighed so deeply she could almost see his mouth go tight. 'I've used the last of the logs. If you doubt it you can check yourself in the morning.'

'But ...'

'If you imagine I'm going outside to replenish the supply and spend hours getting a fire going, then you can think again!'

Her dwindling courage disappearing altogether, Sandra felt so scared she scarcely knew what she was saying. 'I just can't stay here alone with no light!'

'Really?' he drawled, his voice careless, though she could feel the muscles of his arm tensing. 'Then what do you suggest? I've no wish to return to a cold drawing room to keep you company.'

Sandra hesitated nervously, drawing a long steadying

breath. In the face of such encouragement it wasn't easy to go on. 'There—there's a chair in your room.' As soon as she spoke her heartbeats sharpened, but she didn't know what else she could do. Surely it wasn't so outrageous? Wasn't she Stein's wife, and wasn't this a kind of emergency?

'Listen, Sandra,' he was suddenly savage, 'I don't know what sort of game you're playing, but don't expect me to join in! Did no one warn you I'm way past the age for casual frolics with girls who should know better? You could get more than you bargained for.'

'All I want is to be allowed to sit in your room!' Attempting to repudiate what he said, she added recklessly, 'I'm not trying to get you to go to bed with me! I'm just sorry, now, I ever asked!'

'But you did, didn't you, honey,' he sneered, 'and I'm not usually so slow on the uptake. Last night you thought you heard me yell for help, this evening the lights fail. Was it the generator, I wonder, or a dead bulb? Did you contrive this too, and maybe plan to wreck the generator if all else failed?'

Ruthlessly, as he stopped speaking, his hand went to the light switch and, to Sandra's amazement, the whole passage lit up.

'So,' he exclaimed softly, 'it was just one cleverly removed bulb. The others are all working perfectly, are they not? Didn't you know I can make out a slight difference between this and complete darkness?'

Speechlessly, Sandra gazed around, her eyes wide with bewilderment, her face white. When she had gone down for a drink she had left her light on but tightly closed her door for fear Stein should accidentally discover what she was doing. Nor had she put on the lights here, for exactly the same reason, and because she had noticed, by the faint glow, that there was still one burning in the hall—one that Stein must have forgotten as he came up to bed. Hysterical laughter bubbled in her throat. It had never occurred to her that it might only be a bulb!

She stared up at Stein, as if willing the honesty on her face to get through to him. 'I'm sorry, Stein, if that's what you really think of me! I see now I've been rather stupid, but I never thought. I simply presumed it was the generator, after what Thyra said. Do you really think I enjoyed groping around with you in the dark?'

'It almost came off.'

His voice was harsh with anger as he disregarded everything she said, and she shuddered. 'I don't understand, Stein. You don't actually believe I planned all this deliberately so as to spend the night in your room?'

'What else should I think? You have the same acting ability as your cousin.'

'I see.' Feeling shaken to the point of fainting, she turned to leave him. Never had anything seemed as bad as this! 'I'll admit I was stupid not to have checked the lights, but I promise I won't trouble you again. Goodnight, Stein.'

'Oh no, you don't!' Savagely his hand caught her back. 'This time, Mrs Freeman, you can finish what you so shamelessly and confidently began. It's time you learnt you can't go round playing with fire.'

'Stein, put me down!' As he hauled her to him she found sufficient breath to protest but, taking no notice, he lifted her in his arms again, striding with her to his own room.

Half guessing his intention, if unable to accept it, she started hitting him with small, clenched fists. 'I know you're just trying to frighten me,' she cried, 'but if you don't let me go you'll regret it!'

His laughter was harsh as, ignoring her frantic plea, he flung her roughly on the bed. 'Come the morning I might regret a lot of things, but at least there'll be some pleasure to remember—for us both, I hope.'

Oh, God, this was worse than anything she had imagined. The breath was almost knocked out of her as she struggled to escape him on the hard mattress, terrified as his weight imprisoned her and one hard hand pinned her arms above her head. She felt his other hand throwing aside his robe before returning to her trembling limbs. Her own thin nightgown he tore relentlessly from her body.

Every movement he made seemed unhurried but swift and, though her limbs were like water and her heart beating crazily, she felt overwhelmed by a wild terror. It was worse than last night, when she had wanted to comfort him by giving herself and it had been he who had done the rejecting. But even then, when momentarily carried away, he hadn't been like this, so filled with hard determination. Now, as passion surged violently in him, he seemed a stranger.

'Please, Stein,' she begged, groping feverishly for the right words, 'you promised ours would be a marriage in name only. A business arrangement!'

His mouth eased its pressure on her naked shoulder. 'That was before. Since then you've convinced me I'd be a fool not to make the most of this opportunity. You've a beautiful little body, why shouldn't I enjoy it? Why shouldn't I allow you to brighten my dark world? Because that's what it is, my dear wife, no matter how much I might deny it.' His voice softened against her ear. 'You must admit you'd share my pleasure, that you're not altogether indifferent, much as you like to pretend.'

'No!' Horrified at his astuteness, she pushed away from him, 'You've got it all wrong! I'm sorry, Stein.'

'So you should be, you little wildcat!' As her hands escaped and one caught his face, he winced with pain, his brief tenderness forgotten. 'Do you think me quite stupid as well as blind? We had precious little hope of getting our marriage annulled. I think I only realised it this morning, but you must have known all along. I told you before I don't know what sort of game you're playing, but you won't go on playing it with me.'

'I should never have married you!' Half sobbing with an intensity of raw feelings, Sandra struck out at him. 'I hate you, you're a beast! I ...'

He interrupted with cold fury, 'Don't you think you should shut up? Perhaps I'd better do it for you.'

Before she could elude him, he drew her hard against him, his mouth effectively silencing hers. In the next moments Sandra knew she was lost, the tension between them mounting unbearably as he moulded her to him and, if at first she tried to continue her struggles, the expertise of his lovemaking was such, she had no real defence against it. Liquid fire seemed to pour through her veins and she found herself melting helplessly in his arms, her own going suddenly and fiercely around him, drawing him down to her.

She sensed he could be selfish, even cruel if he felt like it, but soon the gentle caressing of his hands, the deep, drugging sweetness of his mouth crushed her fears, awakening an urgency which matched his own. The room and everything in it seemed to fade, she couldn't even hear the wind any more as he swept her insistently towards a passionate surrender. There was only the heavy beating of his heart against hers, the hardening smoothness of his lithe body which had the power to make her feel as she had never felt before.

They seemed to be floating in some way-out universe, one which frightened but also beckoned with promises of ultimate fulfilment as his mouth softened over her trembling lips and he kissed her again and again. As his hand ran down the silken length of her thigh she couldn't seem to resist him and pressed against him hungrily. Her resistance and fright seemed to be fighting a losing battle with her overwhelming love for him. A love which decreed she must do everything she could to make up for the terrible blow fate had dealt him.

Yet, in spite of the flood of desire that consumed her, she wasn't prepared for the searing pain which shattered the ecstasy of their first serious embrace, and she lay shaking and sobbing in his arms when it was all over. It didn't help when, as his breathing grew quiet, he thrust her away from him.

'I'm sorry,' he muttered curtly. 'You should have told me. It seems I've misjudged you.'

She hated what seemed like his rejection of her, hating even more his terse and obviously reluctant apology. She felt cheated, mixed up, not sure what had accompanied the hurt she had suffered. She had seemed to soar, where eagles fly, only to be brought ruthlessly down to earth in the final moment.

'You wouldn't believe me when I tried to explain,' she accused him wildly. 'I had no idea it would like that!'

'It will be better next time,' he said grimly, but his hand was strangely gentle as he reached over to brush a tear from her cheek. 'Sandra,' his voice thickened, 'if I'd known I would have taken more care, but, as I've just told you, it won't be so bad next time.'

Her limbs still aching, she doubted him. 'There won't be a next time!' she declared hysterically, trying, for all she knew he couldn't see, to cover herself with the torn, crumpled sheet.

'There'd better be!' As if not prepared to indulge her any longer, he thrust the sheet aside impatiently, and ran his hands possessively over her. 'Do you think I would let you go now?'

'No!' she cried, secretly ashamed that her body could respond again so soon. The moon was rising and a trail of light fell over the bed, showing dimly the brown nakedness of his strong figure, and she closed her eyes against new and unexpected sensations. If only he loved her as she did him, but all he could think of was his own satisfaction.

'I want to go to my room. Please let me go now, Stein,' she whispered, trying weakly to twist from him.

'No!' Almost as if he read her thoughts, his arms

tightened against her feeble struggles. 'Tonight has proved, has it not, that we can find pleasure in each other, much as you might like to deny it. Right now you feel bruised, disillusioned, but I promise it won't always be like that. I know how your body works now, how you react, and some things are best repeated straight away.'

It was foolish to listen to the clamorous voices within her, the curiosity which wouldn't allow her to leave it alone. She knew she should have left him immediately, that to hesitate could only lead to more anguish, even worse than she suffered now, but, as she raised her hand to protest and her fingers touched his hair-roughened chest, she seemed incapable of movement. She could only cling to him with a low moan, so it appeared that she was begging him to make love to her again and, as he dragged her still closer, she returned his sensuous kisses and caresses until she scarcely knew what she was doing. Until swiftly every part of her seemed to be released before a flood of devastating passion, as they melted together in long minutes of perfect culmination, such as she had never known existed.

In the first light of an early dawn Sandra woke, still feeling dazed, her body aching but languorous. Unsure where she was, she raised herself on one elbow, her heavy eyes widening to find Stein fast asleep beside her. Bemused, she stared down at him. In sleep he looked younger than his thirty-five years and curiously vulnerable. It took an effort to remember that he was no such thing, that he was predatory and very ruthlessly male, yet just then, she could only think how much she loved him.

In the moment it took to realise how she came to be in his bed she felt her throat thicken with tears as she recalled his treatment of her. Of his tenderness which, as she had responded, had rapidly changed to a sensual onslaught of barely controlled passion. If he had sensed her virginal terror behind the response he had sought so assiduously, he had wanted to possess her too much to take any notice.

Apprehensively she held her breath, barely daring to breathe now for fear of disturbing him, but he slept on as if deeply content, one arm flung around her. Still scarcely able to believe last night had really happened, Sandra continued to gaze at him, wondering nervously how he would feel when he woke up. It seemed incredible that one man could have given her such unbelievable delight but, in the sane light of day, it seemed very possible that Stein might not share her feelings.

This morning she felt different, as if his lovemaking had left an indelible mark and she would never be the same again. The feeling of his arms and lips, the low, persuasive timbre of his voice which had hardened each time she had tried to fight him, would be with her for ever. For all his determination to have her whether she was willing or not, he had given her so much in return that her love for him this morning seemed to leave no room for hate.

He moaned, moving restlessly, flinging his free hand over his eyes in a gesture which moved her to compassion. Loving him, she could never regret what she had given him, especially if it helped him to forget the darkness he was forced to live in perpetually. The heartbreak, she suspected, would come later—but she tried not to think of it.

It actually came sooner than she had thought.

'Sophy,' he muttered, and Sandra felt herself grow cold. So Sophy was still on his mind? She, Sandra, was his wife, whom he had loved passionately, but it was still of this other woman he dreamt.

Feeling indescribably cold, she slipped quietly out of bed. A second ago she had been almost overwhelmingly tempted to waken Stein with a soft kiss, but she no longer felt she wanted to be in his arms. Quickly she stepped over her discarded nightdress and ran soundlessly to her own room to seek a robe. Deciding against a bath, she took a quick shower, and it wasn't until the water trickled comfortingly over her that she allowed herself time to think. How foolish she had been to imagine someone like Stein would be faithful to a girl as naïve as herself! If he sought after other women, even in his sleep, what could the future hold? Wouldn't she be wiser to hate rather than love him?

Yet Sandra knew she must be honest. Hadn't she made herself available by her own foolishness? Stein was so ready to think the worst of her. Might he not, this morning, imagine she had acted deliberately, as he had last night? He might even go so far as to think she had intentionally set out to prevent him getting an easy divorce. Being comparatively wealthy he must consider himself a target for every scheming woman.

Unhappily Sandra dried herself and putting on a simple cotton dress, ran downstairs. It might be better to pretend nothing had happened, it might save embarrassment all round. That might not be easy when all she wanted was to be back in Stein's arms, but it might only annoy him if she began to cling. She still had some pride left and must guard against turning into a possessive woman. Besides, she had no excuse to be that way with him.

At the bottom of the stairs she paused, unable to resist trying the lights. Although she prayed rather feverishly that none of them might work, the one in the hall was the only one that didn't. It seemed to confirm or perhaps excuse Stein for making the accusations he had. More than a little disheartened, she removed the spent bulb and went to the kitchen to ask Thyra for another.

Stein joined her as she was finishing her second cup of coffee and she watched bleakly as he deftly helped himself to a large breakfast. She tried to concentrate on pouring his coffee, but could scarcely keep her eyes from him. He made no attempt to kiss or even touch her, which only strengthened her suspicions that he regretted what had taken place.

He did say softly, 'It's a beautiful morning.'

'I expect,' she replied, with effort, 'you'd like to make an early start.'

'Work?' suddenly he smiled broadly. 'Not today. I

didn't think you'd feel like it. I decided we might have a picnic on the beach and forget about work for a change.'

Her breath caught as she envisaged spending the whole day with him down on the warm sands, but it was something she would be wiser not to contemplate. 'We can't, Stein. We haven't finished your third chapter.'

He laughed indifferently, as if sensing the line of her thoughts, his gentle mood, as it so often did, quickly vanishing. 'It's times like this, Sandra, when I'd give almost anything to see your face. Are you a blushing bride this morning, I wonder, or are you as cool and unmoved as you sound? Last night you certainly weren't the latter.'

How dared he tease! He was simply a great brute! 'I think we should forget about last night,' she said sullenly, her aching limbs still with her.

'Why?' his voice sharpened insultingly. 'Did I disappoint you?'

'Please, Stein,' her face went scarlet, 'you know you never intended it should happen ...'

'But it did,' he rasped, 'and you'll find it's something which can't be undone.'

'But not something that need be repeated.'

Again he laughed unkindly. 'Ah, Sandra, why should I bother to argue with you this morning when you might be very ready to seek my arms again tonight? I'm not very good at making love over a breakfast table, nor do I find it an easy subject to discuss with someone I can't see. But my memory doesn't play me tricks. I can recall quite lucidly how you were in my bed, especially after you'd been there a while. I'd think very carefully about rejecting me now— you may not want to later.'

Mortified, Sandra stared at him, feeling completely shaken, her cheeks even hotter. She didn't want to remember how it had been in his arms through the night and, when he could only dream of Sophy, it was unfair of him to remind her. 'I still think,' she insisted tearfully, 'it would be better forgotten.'

Putting down his knife and fork, as if losing interest in his food, he leant towards her. 'How do you propose going about it?' he jeered.

'Men!' she gulped, stumbling to her feet. 'You make love to me while you love another woman! I wonder how you can do it?'

Getting up himself, he halted abruptly beside her. 'So that's your opinion of me?'

She found it difficult to be so near and not touch him. Her voice wobbled infuriatingly. 'If I dislike you it's your own fault!'

With a sigh his hands descended on her shoulders. 'You're a very lovely girl, Sandra—not one a man would tire of easily, but you have a lot to learn, about men in particular. This morning, when I woke, I wanted you with me, but you were gone. Why should I have had the feeling of a ship without its anchor? Such a small thing to become so necessary. Just don't let me wake again and not find you there.'

'Don't make me, Stein,' she begged breathlessly, her face suddenly white with emotion. 'You wouldn't like to think I was only there because of your orders. You've always made it clear that you hate me and my cousin, so you can't possibly want me!'

She didn't know why she had brought it up, but the damage was done before she could retract. 'Sure,' he drawled, gazing down on her dryly, 'but hate can sometimes make one feel more intensely than love. It certainly won't make me reject one inch of your enticing little body. I can enjoy that even while I'm hating you.'

They had their picnic after all and, over the next week or two, Sandra found that it was difficult to escape him. Stein appeared to have the uncanny ability of finding her whenever he wanted to and there seemed nothing she could do to prevent it. Shamefully she realised his love-making was rapidly becoming something she didn't want to be without, if she wasn't quite ready yet to admit the truth of what he had told her. The nights she spent in his arms were interludes to be treasured, stored against the time which would undoubtedly come, when he no longer wanted her.

Sandra knew he would never say he loved her, and, while she respected him for not pretending to in order to get his own way, her heart was sore. He made love to her most nights, but she knew she would never hear such magic words pass his lips. Sometimes, when he held her, she felt her love for him moving through her almost tangibly and knew a wild jealousy of those women he had really cared for, a hostile envy of the rapture they must have known. When she had first come to the island none of this seemed to matter so much, but since she had begun sharing Stein's bed she found such primitive reactions more difficult to control. He mustn't guess how she often felt like shouting at him, of accusing him of things which had never previously occurred to her. It was enough that she should be horrified by her own hysterical emotions without having his withering opinion too.

Wanting only to love him, she was forced to endure his continuing derision regarding her conduct and Alexandra's. Always he reminded her that their relationship could only be physical, even while making it no secret that he needed her more and more, and though her pride felt humbled into the dust she couldn't find any strength to resist him.

Sometimes she felt so wounded by what he said she wondered how much longer she could endure it. She grew too pale and lost weight. She guessed Thyra had noticed and told Stein, because he suddenly insisted she go out more. He said he wished he could have taken her around the island, to meet the people, but was not sure enough of himself for this. He didn't fancy falling over them as he introduced them to his wife. He wasn't bitter so much as cynical. Often Sandra wished he would be bitter—it might have made him seem more human. He might be easier to live with if he had a few noticeable faults and failings, such things as Gran had always been on about. He did take her down to the beach more often, though, and with the smooth sand hot under her back and Stein stretched out by her side she felt oddly content. Very often, while she lay half asleep, he would begin making love to her, and then she loved the taste of brine on his mouth; the smell of sand on his bare skin; the harshness of it against hers as he pressed her passionately into it.

Once he had taken her out sailing in his caique, but naturally had to leave the skippering of it to Panos, and, though he didn't say anything, Sandra sensed his impatience at not being able to do the sailing himself. He had sat in the prow with her, his arm lightly around her waist, the wind warm on their faces, and she wondered if he felt resentful that she could see the dancing waves while he could not. They had cruised among the islands that day, with small fish of many colours darting alongside them. The water had been the most vivid blue imaginable and, somehow, she had managed to be cheerful, so he should not have the least suspicion of how her heart ached for him.

They did some work on his book, but not much. Mysteriously Stein seemed to lose the inclination to concentrate on it. One afternoon, when he did get down to doing a little revising in the study, he told her he might be leaving Kalnos for a week or two.

'I'm going to London, possibly for an operation,' he shrugged, almost as if he were discussing the weather. 'There might be a chance of regaining my sight.'

It seemed several seconds before Sandra could speak, before she could pull herself together sufficiently to answer. She felt shocked, consumed by a great anxiety, but was glad he had no idea how his abruptly given news distressed her. 'You didn't have to spring it on me like that,' she protested apprehensively. 'Isn't there a risk? Shouldn't you have tests?'

Laconically he grunted, 'I had those some time ago.'

'Then why—why have you waited?'

Again he shrugged. 'I'm not sure. Perhaps I couldn't make up my mind.'

She had a suspicion this wasn't the true reason, but she was more concerned with the danger. 'I asked if there wasn't a risk.'

He turned towards the window. 'If there's any chance of being able to see again I think I should take it. Nothing can be guaranteed, of course, but I've decided to give it a go. I've little to lose. I sent word with the helicopter when it brought the mail last week. When it returns I expect to hear they can take me and will probably leave immediately.'

Sandra felt an excruciating anguish, so real she might have fainted. How could he talk so casually about anything so serious? He discussed it as lightly as if he were contemplating a day's fishing!

When she didn't reply at once he came back, reaching for her, his voice harsh as he drew her up to him. 'What's the matter, girl? Don't you like the idea of my being able to see? You won't be able to hide so much from me then.'

'Oh, shut up!' Her feelings in a turmoil, she apologised bleakly, 'I'm sorry, Stein, but you never tell me anything! How many times have I asked about your eyes? How often would I willingly have given mine so you might see!' Her voice rose passionately. 'You've always refused to discuss anything. You could at least have told me about the tests! Now you spring the whole lot on me—and in such a manner.'

'If I didn't talk about it,' he returned grimly, 'it was because there were things I wanted to forget. And, if you'd known, perhaps you wouldn't have married me and I shouldn't have had the revenge I craved. Your concern might move me,' he jeered, 'if I were able to believe it was genuine.'

Dispirited, Sandra gazed at him. He probably couldn't wait to get a divorce and continue his broken association with Sophy. Once his sight was returned and he was free again that should be easy. 'However much you wanted revenge it could scarcely have been worth the trouble of getting married to me, of coming here,' she said painfully.

'That's a matter of opinion,' he replied cryptically.

'Stein?' He must feel her trembling, but she couldn't help it. She must ignore his cruel words, but she couldn't take no notice of the fear in her heart. Fear which seemed to be taking over completely. Her hands clutched at him, as if full of the frantic strength of her own torment. 'If there's any risk I'd rather you didn't have this operation. I wouldn't mind staying here with you for ever.'

His laughter was crucifying, as was the harsh twist of his mouth that went with it. 'What a charmingly generous suggestion, my dear. Am I supposed to be grateful? Is half a loaf so much better than no bread at all that you feel forced to make such an offer? I don't doubt you find your present way of life very comfortable, but I assure you, you will be well enough compensated to resume living in England in much the same manner.'

Aghast, she shrank back. Stein, like this, was a stranger. There seemed nothing left to say, and hadn't she humiliated herself enough? What more did he expect of her? 'I'm sorry,' she said numbly, 'if I've been stupidly obtrusive. Of course you must go to London. When is the helicopter coming? I must pack our things.'

'I expect it any time,' he replied coolly, removing her clinging hands, 'but there's no question of you coming to London. My old friend Professor Manoli is coming with me. You will go back to Corfu and stay with my grand-mother.'

# CHAPTER NINE

THE helicopter arrived next day. By this time Sandra was all packed and waiting, resigned in a way she scarcely understood herself. The shock of Stein's announcement about his operation hadn't abated, but she forced herself to face up to it. He had left her with little other option; no amount of pleading had moved him, he refused to listen. Quite clearly he didn't want her, and she had no other course but to agree to go to Corfu.

Last night she had felt so miserable that she had gone to her old room. She hadn't known whether she meant to stay. She had actually cried herself to sleep, and whether or not Stein had come looking for her she didn't know. When she woke that morning she had still been alone, alone and curiously beset by haunting fears. It was as if Stein had already decided that the brief interlude on Kalnos was over and the sooner he made a start of severing their odd relationship the better.

At breakfast Thyra mentioned that he had gone with Panos to the village on business but would be back in time to go with Madame when the mail arrived. It surprised Sandra that he was so confident that the news he awaited would come this morning, but it did, and she suspected his arrangements must have been at least half made some time ago.

She bade Thyra and Panos, the only two islanders she had really got to know, goodbye. Stein must have said why they were going but the woman was cheerful and seemed as though she expected them back quite soon. Sandra didn't disillusion her.

In the helicopter Stein told her a little more. Professor

Manoli would be waiting on Corfu; tomorrow they would leave for England. Sandra must stay on Corfu where he would arrange to let her know the outcome of his operation. As soon as he was able he would endeavour to get their marriage sorted out and see she was well provided for. Until then she must stay where he could be sure she was being well looked after. He was strangely remote, his curtly given advice seeming more like an order, and far from re-assuring it only made her more miserable.

It seemed rather noisy at the villa after the remote quiet-ness of Kalnos. Madame Kartalis was in her element, fuss-ing over Stein and entertaining the Professor. Sophy called later in the afternoon, as did Madame Nikitiadis and her two daughters, and Stein appeared to regard this miniature invasion quite calmly. Sandra thought he might have been annoyed that his grandmother had so obviously spread the news of his operation but, if he was, he raised no verbal objection. Not while Sandra was around, anyway.

While she was around he took the opportunity to be de-risive about other things. It hadn't occurred to her that, this time, she might naturally be expected to share Stein's old room, and she changed swiftly for dinner in order to avoid him when he came up. For once she felt grateful that Sophy was keeping him engaged in a lengthy conversation. Sandra was pleased she was quite ready, just laying his shirt out on the bed when he came and, after he had thanked her sarcastically for still continuing her wifely duties, she plucked up courage to tackle him about it.

'If you had a word with Katrina,' she suggested nerv-ously, 'I'm sure she could find me something somewhere else.'

When he promised, mildly enough, to see what he could do she felt both dispirited and relieved. 'I'll leave it to you, then.' She made an effort to speak lightly, as she turned to leave him, and wasn't prepared that he should catch her wrist as she paused.

'So now you're away from the island you find any thought of sharing my room distasteful?'

His darkly handsome face was so hard she dared do nothing but be evasive. 'I'd scarcely put it so bluntly.'

'No?' His hand tightened, sliding up her bare arm as he pulled her against him, with little regard for her carefully neat toilet. He didn't kiss her but dropped his head to her slender shoulder, breathing in deeply the delicate perfume of her skin. 'So you've decided to keep me at a distance? Have you forgotten how much you enjoy being in my arms? You can't hide the way I'm able to make you feel, you can be a shameless little hussy when you like.'

Indignation caused her to gasp, as she tried to escape the blatant seduction of his wandering mouth. 'I think you've a nerve speaking like that, when you've done nothing but talk of divorce! I suppose you feel you can make love to both me and Sophy and get away with it?'

'But she isn't my wife,' he taunted, 'and it seems sense that I should make do with the one I have at the moment. A bird in the hand—remember?'

She wouldn't believe he could be so callous, especially to someone whose heart was bursting with love and concern for him. Hate welled, beating down every other emotion.

'You're beastly!' she cried, wrenching away from him. 'I think perhaps I'll be well rid of you!'

'I wouldn't be in such a hurry,' he advised. 'It might be wiser to wait a few weeks.'

'I suppose you mean because of your operation?' Hardening her heart still further, she exclaimed bitterly, 'Always your convenience!'

'Not only that,' he returned suavely. 'Have you ever thought there could be any repercussions to the nights you've spent in my arms?'

'Oh, no!' She felt her lips go white, her whole body cold even to think of it. If Stein had loved her—she stared at him blankly, a pulse beating frantically at the base of her throat—she wouldn't have minded. In fact, she couldn't think of anything she might have wanted more, but not this way. Never like this!

Stein, as if mistaking her silence for horror, pursued cruelly, 'You wouldn't want my child, but neither would you want to have it alone. Heaven knows we haven't done anything to prevent it happening, and you didn't remind me. Just another snare you probably set to entrap me.'

The evening meal, served late and by candlelight, seemed the longest Sandra had ever sat through. Her mind seemed frozen, along with every other part of her, and she hoped feverishly that Stein's suspicions would be proved untrue. She couldn't bear to contemplate a future with Stein feeling forced to remain by her side, trapped, as he said, by his own folly! Yet in spite of his contempt she found her gaze returning to him constantly as he sat by Sophy's side, apparently enjoying the meal, Sandra thought despairingly, that threatened to choke her.

While they were drinking coffee she managed to speak to Professor Manoli, to ask him about Stein's operation. When he hesitated, she pressed urgently, 'I won't pretend he's given me anything but the bare facts. He doesn't seem to realise how worried I am.'

Again he was reluctant, his frown emphasising his discomfort. 'If he really doesn't want you to know about it ...'

'But I must!'

'My dear child,' the Professor looked long and intently into her flushed, unhappy face, her wide, anxious eyes, 'surely it is wrong to persist. If your husband won't ...'

'Professor!' she interrupted without apology, 'I'm not asking you to give away professional secrets. I would just like to be told briefly what's involved, how much danger there'll be. Stein merely shrugs it all off, just like a visit to the dentist.'

After another moment's scrutiny Professor Manoli smiled sympathetically. Taking her arm, he led her out on to the terrace. 'I'm sure there's not that much need for secrecy, my dear. The eye, as you must know, is an extremely delicate instrument, a highly specialised receptor of the nervous system and, once damaged can lead to all sorts of complications, complete loss of sight being perhaps the worst of them ...'

The professor wasn't particularly long-winded and it didn't really take him long to explain how Stein's accident had damaged the optic nerves, but subsequent tests had proved that some of the damage, in his case, had healed, providing a condition where an operation was possible. An operation which might, if successful, give Stein back his sight.

'Is there—will there be any danger?' Sandra faltered, when he had finished, the thickness of tears in her voice, a bitter taste of nausea in her mouth.

'I'd be a fool to pretend there wasn't a certain element of risk in any operation,' he said bluntly. 'There are very few things we can guarantee absolutely, but danger is a word I prefer not to use. Just remember this is his decision and he can be no worse off, if he's no better. But he has the indomitable spirit, your husband, child. I have known him all his life.'

He maybe needed it, she guessed shrewdly, while feeling very indebted to the Professor, to whom she bade a grateful goodnight.

It was later than she thought, most of the guests being gone by the time she returned from the terrace, and she ran upstairs, leaving Stein to drink a nightcap with Professor Manoli. Madame Kartalis appeared also to have retired.

Daringly, Sandra peeped into her old room, only to find it must have been given to the Professor as his things were strewn around, his books piled on the table beside the bed. There could be no hope for her here.

Tensely she retraced her steps to Stein's room, waiting

for him, feeling too overwrought to relax, especially after her conversation with the Professor. He had meant to be reassuring—he had been reassuring; it was just the whole idea of Stein's operation, that he might have to suffer pain, which was getting her down. Yet this couldn't in any way change the personal situation between them, so she must wait until Stein came, to ask if he had made other sleeping arrangements.

She was startled that he followed her very quickly, but aghast when he told her there was no other suitable room. The only other available one had been given to a maid who had been called in to help with the extra guests.

'I could always go and sleep with her,' he grinned, 'if she'd have me.'

Sandra flushed, recalling how the girl had stared at him while she helped to serve dinner. It was proof, if she needed any, that Stein was still very attractive to most women.

'I wish you'd be sensible for a change,' she retorted sharply, tearing her eyes away from the dark ruggedness of him. 'I'm sure, with your ingenuity, you could have managed something!'

Unrepentantly he grinned, strolling across to her where she stood with her back to the dressing table, gazing at him stonily, trying to hide her unhappiness. 'Go and have your bath,' he said soothingly. 'By the time you've finished I'm sure to have thought of something.'

In the bathroom, deep in a tubful of warm water, she tried to relax. She couldn't gauge his exact mood but decided to trust him. She closed her eyes, rubbing a tired, damp hand over her face. He probably intended sleeping downstairs in his grandmother's extremely comfortable sitting room. He must have known of her conversation with the Professor on the terrace. That he hadn't been angry seemed a good sign—he might be amenable.

With her eyes closed and lulled into a state of false security, she didn't hear him come in. It wasn't until she felt the water drain from the bath that she saw him standing over her, dangling the bath plug.

'You've been there long enough,' he grunted. 'I told you to have a bath, not sleep in it!'

Trying desperately to remember that he couldn't actually see her, even though his eyes seemed to glint over her, she snapped, 'Maybe you're going to do that?'

He laughed coldly, then, to her consternation, bent down and scooped her up. 'Not likely! I'm going to sleep with you, my dear. I thought I could resist the temptation, all things considered, but I find I can't.'

Her breath caught as she lay, momentarily transfixed, staring up at his face, his arms tightly around her damp body. 'Stein, you know it's all over. You said so yourself. I'd much prefer to have my hand cut off with one blow, rather than ...' Full of a terrible confusion, a perplexity at what she had been about to say, she trailed off.

'You talk too much, Madame.' He sounded curiously husky, and she had a brief glimpse of a lean, smooth cheek before a firm, well cut mouth descended on hers.

His touch filled her with ecstasy. A quiver ran through her, to every sensitive nerve in her body, as he kissed her possessively. She wanted him to kiss her but, while physically she seemed unable to resist him, her mind rebelled— so much so that she tried to evade him as he carried her towards his bed. 'Don't, Stein!' she tried to make one last protest. 'You'll only regret it!'

'Stop struggling!' His mouth crushed hers roughly so that when he released her she was breathless and flushed, 'Would you refuse to appease me? Perhaps a doomed man!'

'Don't!' It was a moan of anguish she couldn't control, though she realised he was merely taunting.

He put a hand under her chin, lifting her face. 'I promise it won't be as bad as that.' Removing his robe quickly, he slid down beside her, his arms going around her again. 'You don't know how much I'm looking forward to being able to see you properly, my small Sandra.'

'I'm very plain,' she gasped, the familiar reaction starting up in her limbs as a flame whipped up between them. Feeling rippled over her as warm as the sun.

'You aren't plain at all,' he contradicted, his voice thickening as his hand went to her breasts. 'You're slender and beautifully shaped, as I've told you before. You're very easy to love.'

Still she tried to fight him, as she always felt uneasily dismayed by the clamorous instincts of her too responsive body. But he was mature and experienced and dealt with her tentative rebellion ruthlessly. His mouth was insistent on her lips as he pulled her firmly against him, until the room began to spin crazily around her and she felt herself soaring wildly above it. His grip was cruel on her soft skin, but suddenly she wanted him so feverishly she didn't care. Her lips responded to the demanding passion of his and, with a small moan, she gave herself to him completely.

He made love to her that night as if he might never see her again, and an early dawn broke before they slept.

Hours later she woke, with the dreadful feeling that she was in the middle of a nightmare, to find him gone. As he usually rose early she tried to dismiss her apprehension by telling herself she would find him in the garden, but when she ran to the window she could not see him anywhere. As her eyes searched in vain for his tall figure a sudden coldness crowded out the new warmth in her heart. She had known he was leaving this morning, but surely he couldn't have gone without saying goodbye, not after last night. Everything must be different between them now. He hadn't said anything, but his lovemaking had seemed like a revelation and she had began to hope. Remembering the tenderness of his lips against her cheek as she had finally fallen asleep, she had felt sure she had come to mean something important to him. So strong was the impression that she could not immediately dismiss it, for all her instinctive feeling of dread. Dressing quickly, she brushed her hair into some semblance of tidiness and flew downstairs. Perhaps Stein was just having breakfast.

Katrina was in the hall. 'Kyrios Stein,' Sandra gasped, breathlessly. 'And the Professor?'

'But madame, they've gone!' Katrina's face was a study of dismay as Sandra's went white. 'Didn't you know, madame? The *kyrios* told me you were tired and not to wake you. I supposed he had already said goodbye?'

'Yes, yes, of course,' Sandra stammered, turning from Katrina's anxious regard. 'It was just that I had—hoped to catch him.' How could she explain to Katrina that she had hoped to change Stein's mind about taking her? How, as he had held her in his arms, during those rapturous, starlit hours, she had become confident of her ability to sway him. If only she hadn't overslept!

'What time did they go?' she asked slowly, regaining a little composure.

'About an hour ago, madame. They left early to catch the connection in Athens.'

'Yes—I know about that!' She didn't mean to sound impatient, but her heart was sore.

'Oh, I almost forgot,' Katrina's crestfallen face was suddenly all smiles, 'there is a note for you. The kyrios Stein said you were to have it as soon as you rose.'

Sandra thanked her gratefully, trying to make up for her former abruptness, before going into the drawing room to read what Stein had left. He must have thought of her after all, and her spirits lightened a little. The envelope lay on a small table immediately within the door. There was nothing about it to indicate the shock she was about to receive.

'Sandra,' the note ran, 'don't try to follow me. The interlude of our marriage has been pleasanter than I expected, but most things have to come to an end. What I have said previously still stands, although there is no need to say anything to Grandmother as yet. In a week or two I will contact you. In the meantime, thanks for everything.'

Shock made Sandra sway unsteadily as she read the brief missive again. She could scarcely take it in, but after a few minutes when she did, anger spread flags of bright colour across her pale cheeks. So he thought he could pick her up and then discard her, just like that! Blindly she stared at the white sheet of paper in her hand, the strong, masculine handwriting which sprawled a little because Stein couldn't see, and her flicker of anger died as quickly as it had risen. Of course he could, she realised bitterly; he could do what he liked and there wasn't a thing she could do about it. Every small hope he had raised through the night died a painful death. He had simply acted as many men might have done in his position, considering her own responsiveness. She really meant nothing to him, this note proved it. She had been a fool to think otherwise.

Yet none of this stopped her from asking Madame Kartalis, when she came down, how long she would advise her to wait before ringing the hospital. Compared with her anxiety, pride became meaningless and she knew she must know how Stein was, even if her enquiries made him angry. She need not give her name if it was to upset him, she could pretend to be acting on behalf of his grandmother.

Madame Kartalis frowned. 'I should leave it until tomorrow, or perhaps longer. You know how Stein hates a fuss.'

'But I am his wife,' Sandra protested, with a dignity which sat oddly on her young shoulders.

The old lady looked at her sharply. 'I don't know why you weren't as insistent about going with him.'

Sandra glanced at her warily, feeling curiously exhausted. 'You must know he wouldn't let me. It's not that I didn't want to go.'

Madame sat down abruptly. 'Young people today bewilder me,' she announced heavily. 'Nothing would have kept me from Stein's grandfather.'

In a peculiar fashion these words were to haunt Sandra all day. Stein had promised to let her know how he was, but she guessed he wouldn't do this before his operation and it made sense that it would be impossible for him to do so afterwards, at least for some time. She had intended asking the Professor this morning how long it would be before they knew if Stein's operation had been a success. Oh, why had she overslept? By allowing herself to become so intoxicated with love she had, inadvertently, missed any opportunity of finding out all the important things she should have known!

On the morning of the second day Sandra knew she could stay at the villa no longer. She must go to London so that, if nothing else, she could be near him. Last night, when she rang the famous London clinic where he had gone, they had told her he had not yet had an operation, but when she had asked to speak to him, they said he was not taking any calls. She wondered if their attitude might have been different if she had said she was his wife, but somehow she hadn't found the courage.

This didn't stop her from thinking seriously of making a lengthy journey just to be with him. She still had his cruel note, but that didn't seem to make any difference. Once he was well it wouldn't matter if he still wanted to discard her. All things considered, it would probably be wiser not to live together when he didn't love her, but in the meantime, she must be with him.

When she told Madame Kartalis of her intentions, the old lady did nothing to discourage her. This could mean, Sandra realised dryly, that her grandmother-in-law would be pleased to see the last of her. On the other hand, since Stein had left, she had not been entirely unkind.

To acquaint the old lady of her plans, Sandra invaded her bedroom. 'I'm sorry to have disturbed you at this hour,' she apologised awkwardly, 'but if Thimios could take me to the airport I might, with luck, find a seat on a plane from Athens today.'

It was agreed that Thimios should take her, but there was little time to spare. 'We must hurry,' he urged, as Sandra made her brief farewells to the household. 'In this part of the island the mountain roads are not made for speed.'

Afterwards Sandra was to recall his words. Thimios was an excellent driver but, like most continentals, he drove fast. Once away from the villa he appeared to forget his warning about the mountain roads and accelerated hard. In the short time Sandra had been here she had grown used to such excessive bursts of speed, though she still felt slightly nervous. Today, however, she urged Thimios to go even faster, as she sat anxiously in the front seat beside him.

'Please, Thimios, I must catch an early plane, otherwise I might be stranded in Athens until tomorrow. I must get to Stein!'

'You leave it to me.' Thimios accelerated again, as if the mention of Stein's name had smitten him with the same sense of urgency. 'I'll see you catch the very first, Madame Sandra.'

How the accident happened exactly, Sandra never knew. It had a lot to do, Thimios told her afterwards, with a lunatic coming towards them equally fast, but nothing was ever proved or made clear. The last she remembered was flying forward or sideways, she wasn't sure which, and of Thimios giving a loud, angry shout. Then everything went black and she knew no more.

Her first impression, on coming around in hospital, was of wonder, of being in a cool, peaceful place, but of it being wholly unfamiliar. It took her only minutes to realise she was in hospital and, immediately thinking of Stein, she tried to struggle up.

'Where am I?' she cried.

'Hush, madame.' At once by her side was a pleasant, white-coated nurse with excellent English. As Sandra turned towards her she laid cool, professional fingers on her brow. 'You must not excite yourself, madame. You have been in an accident and have suffered concussion, but otherwise you are very well.'

An accident—concussion! Unable to believe it, Sandra moved her head incredulously but winced at the pain that shot through it. Whatever else had suffered injury, there was nothing wrong with her memory. Everything came rushing back. 'The car—Thimios?' she gasped, trying to sit up again, only to be held firmly against her pillows.

'The driver is all right, madame. Please not to upset yourself. He only suffered scratches, as did the car. We Greeks are a tough lot, madame.'

'But what happened?'

'Unfortunately you were thrown out, Madame Freeman.' A doctor came up on her other side, taking over from the nurse with an authoritative smile. 'You must not alarm yourself about this. You are being well taken care of.'

'My husband?' Sandra could no longer hold back from asking.

The doctor smiled slightly, as if recognising her anxiety. 'I believe, madame, his grandmother, Madame Kartalis, has been in touch with him. She told me that when you recovered consciousness I was to tell you he has had his operation and is as well as can be expected.'

'His sight?' She had never thought a single question could be so painful to ask. Perspiration broke out on her brow and her pulse was racing, she could tell by the way in which the doctor frowned as he took a light hold of her wrist.

'I must ask you again not to excite yourself, Mrs Freeman. Madame Kartalis said it was too early to tell.'

'I see.' Defeated, Sandra closed her eyes, her head throbbing. It seemed ironical that, after all her efforts, she hadn't managed to get to Stein. She hadn't been there when he most needed her. Dully she lifted heavy lashes, gazing at the doctor, who still remained anxiously by her bed. 'How long do I need to stay here, doctor? I must get to London as quickly as possible. You do see?'

His frown deepened at her obvious agitation, though his eyes were compassionate. 'I do understand, madame, but I am afraid it will be some days before you are well enough to travel. Very soon, of course, you may leave hospital and return to the care of Madame Kartalis.'

Exactly eight days after leaving it, Sandra went back to the villa. Ignominiously, she thought, her spirits at a lower ebb than she could ever remember. It was only to be expected, Madame Kartalis said, that Sandra should feel shaken, but she agreed with the doctor it was nothing a few days' good care shouldn't cure. Katrina and Thimios welcomed her, the latter most apologetically, but it was their concern that warmed her more than anything else.

In hospital it had been the lack of some definite news of Stein which had worried Sandra far more than her own health. She was young and would soon recover from a small accident. When Madame Kartalis had eventually told her, over the telephone, that his operation had been a success, she had had her suspicions the old lady had known for some time. In spite of this Sandra had felt a warm glow in her heart that Stein should once more have his sight. She had felt utterly and completely grateful. When she had asked Madame Kartalis if she had told Stein about her accident, the old lady had been extremely evasive.

'No,' she said now, when Sandra repeated her query. 'How could I?' She glanced away, but Sandra noticed how her eyes glinted with cunning. 'Would you liked to have been responsible for his possible reactions, girl? A shock in the middle of such a delicate operation could have had serious repercussions.'

Silently Sandra digested this, knowing she should have

thought of it herself. She seemed to have got everything in such a dreadful muddle. 'I understand,' she replied, dismally, 'but what must he have thought when I didn't so much as ring to ask how he was?'

'You worry unnecessarily.' Madame smiled quietly. 'Sophy is in London. She promised to call and see him. In fact, I did not have to press her, she could not get there fast enough. To stand in for you, of course.'

Sandra bore such understated criticism stoically. While she would like to have cried sharply that she loved Stein desperately—possibly a lot more than Sophy did—she realised Stein didn't love her. He had married her, made use of her, but that was all. Like many men he had given in to the temptation of proximity but, no matter how he had chosen to treat her, she had never been able to hate him for long. But he need not worry that she would hold him to his wedding day promises, nor would he have to worry any longer that she might be going to have his child. Her accident had put an end to that, if there had ever been any possibility in the first place.

Restlessly she moved across the room, unaware of Madame Kartalis's eyes on her white face, unconscious of anything but her own distraught feelings. Sophy in London, oozing with sympathy, and Stein already very much in love with her. Clearly she could imagine Stein back at the flat, Sophy with him, perhaps making herself available in every way. What chance then for a wife whom he hated?

Madame was speaking again. 'Dear Sophy is eventually going back to America. She simply left a week or two earlier in order to help Stein.'

'How very kind of her!' Sandra flared, unable to restrain an impetuous sarcasm.

Madame ignored this. 'Do you intend journeying to London child, after you are fully recovered?'

Sandra wished she would stop referring to her as a child. It made her feel about ten years old and just as responsible! 'I must,' she answered shortly.

'You love him, don't you, Sandra?'

'Love him?' The query, coming from such an unexpected source, startled her. Quickly Sandra tried to prevent betraying emotions from clouding her hot face. 'Of course,' she confessed stiffly, feeling no need to tell Madame Kartalis how much. 'Otherwise I shouldn't have married him. Isn't it natural that a wife should love her husband?' she asked defensively.

A slight smile of satisfaction went unnoticed on Madame's lips. 'One would imagine this should be so,' she agreed, with a suaveness strangely reminiscent of Stein's. 'Perhaps it is the quality of love which is changing.'

'I'm not sure that Stein loves me.' There, it was out at last! An honest confession, not one she had intended making, but the time for pretence seemed past. Bleakly she glanced at her tormentor. If nothing else it should please the old lady.

'There's only one way to find out, is there not?' Far from looking pleased, Madame Kartalis stared at her briskly, her finger on the bell for Katrina. 'Go to him. Go as soon as possible. Didn't you give him your Pandora's box when you married him?'

'My Pandora's box, madame?'

'Yes. There are many versions in Greek mythology, child, so I will choose the one I like best. When Epimetheus married the beautiful Pandora and he opened the box she gave him, all the evils flew out, but there remained hope. I am not sure, my dear, what else Stein had when he left here. Certainly his mood was unpredictable, but I do believe he had this, and that it was, in some strange way, not altogether to do with his eyesight.'

It was raining when Sandra arrived back in London. The skies were grey, more like winter than early summer, and she thought ruefully of the warm sunshine she had just left behind. Since this was England, she was aware, it wouldn't be long before the clouds broke and the day became fine again, but, like her own affairs, that could take time.

She took a taxi from the airport, giving the driver the address of Stein's flat. Stein might be there as he had left the clinic. Sandra knew this as she had rung from Athens the night before. The person to whom she had spoken had told her he was well and was leaving hospital next day. When Sandra had asked to speak to him personally, the nurse had returned to tell her he was occupied with a visitor and sent his apologies. Naturally the nurse had sounded extremely embarrassed that a patient declined to spare even a moment for his obviously anxious wife, but she was too well trained to pass any comment. If she hadn't turned so cool Sandra might have asked what Stein's visitor was like. As it was, she thought she could guess.

Her spirits low, she stared blindly at the swishing windscreen wipers, as they dealt bravely with each fresh onslaught. Could Stein really see now? A great surge of grateful delight ran through her as she contemplated such a miracle. The nurse had insisted that he was well but, apart from his eyes, he had always been in a wonderful physical condition ever since Sandra had known him. He was tough, virile, with a great strength to his lean, athletic body, but might not the mental strain of the operation he had been through be severe? Should she not, as his wife, have gone to the clinic and had a talk with the surgeon who had performed the operation? What must they have thought of her continuing absence, of her never so much as contacting them by telephone during the first crucial days? Those days when, unknown to them, she had lain in her own hospital bed, unconscious.

Nervously she drew a quick breath and sat back, instead of giving the driver fresh orders to go to the clinic. She must remember she was not a normal wife. Hadn't Stein's refusal to so much as speak to her last night emphasised that? He wouldn't understand if she consulted the hospital, started asking a lot of questions. He would merely consider it none of her business. He might even go so far as to complain to the hospital about it, and she dared not risk that.

It was an almost tangible fear of Stein's reactions which kept her to her first decision to go to his flat. She knew he hadn't another place in England because he had told her he had sold his house here before going to America to make his last film. In the interval, between then and his accident, he had not been able to decide whether to settle more or less permanently on Kalnos or buy something else here, perhaps in the country. This must have been when he had expected to marry Alexandra.

Bleakly Sandra wondered how he would arrange his life now. She supposed one of the first things he would see about was getting a divorce. With his sight returned and his freedom there might be no limits to his future achievements. There was his writing and the films which would no doubt continue to be made from his increasingly popular books and, way above everything else, there would be Sophy. Another marriage, this time with no unhappiness attached, would give him contentment and maybe inspire him to even greater heights. There would be no place for a girl like Sandra Weir, not even in his memories.

Trying to ignore the increasing ache in her heart, Sandra crouched in the corner of the cab, not bothering to so much as hope any more that her own future could hold anything else but a desperate loneliness.

# CHAPTER TEN

STANDING outside the door, the taxi paid off, her finger apprehensively on the doorbell, reminded Sandra so much of her first visits to Stein's flat that her courage almost failed her. How much easier to turn and flee, to leave all future contact with him to a solicitor. Wouldn't it be better not to see him again? A swift, decisive break might not be half as painful.

Yet the thought of not seeing him again convulsively tautened her hesitating finger, making the decision for her. Her whole body rigid with nervous tension, she heard the faintly melodious chimes echoing inside and, before she had any chance of disappearing, found herself staring straight at the one person she had hoped not to see—Sophy.

'Oh, good evening!' Sophy's smile was completely sophisticated. She looked like a sleek, well fed cat. 'I wondered,' she drawled, 'when you would decide to turn up.'

'You must have known why I wasn't able to come sooner,' Sandra retorted quickly, wondering how she was going to get inside, with Sophy effectively blocking the way. Did she just wait on the doorstep until Sophy chose to stand aside, or should she push past her and demand to know where Stein was? From here she could see nothing of him. Perhaps he wasn't here. He could have loaned the place to Sophy and gone elsewhere. No—she bit her lip sharply—that would be too much to hope for. Sophy was surely dressed and made up much more attractively than she would have been if there hadn't been a man inside the flat. Trying to speak as coolly as the other girl, she added, 'Now that I am here I would like to see Stein right away.'

'I'm afraid he is having his bath. I was just about to go and see if he was managing all right.'

Sandra's face paled. 'Then he isn't properly recovered?'

'Oh yes!' Sophy's laughter tinkled lightly. 'There is nothing much wrong with him now, my dear. I think it is merely reaction to several things. You must remember what he has just been through.'

'Yes, of course.' Relief swept aside Sophy's superior tones, but under the relief there was an unconscious dread. What exactly was Sophy's position here? Her manner, if nothing else, seemed wholly possessive. 'I—Madame Kartalis said you were on your way to America.'

'I am.'

'Then——' Sandra could scarcely put it into words, 'I mean why, if that's so, are you staying here? If you are actually staying here?'

'I was.' Morosely Sophy stared at her. 'And I don't think I need to apologise. I didn't feel it right to leave Stein alone, especially when he talked of getting a divorce.'

'He told you that!'

Feeling suddenly faint, as if even the floor was about to jump up and hit her, Sandra pushed blindly past Sophy into the hall, at precisely the same moment as Stein stepped out of the bathroom. He wore a short dressing gown of black silk, tied tight to his lean waist and powerful thighs, and looked much the same as he had ever done. Only his eyes were different. Stunned to a blank, gasping silence, Sandra realised it. Now they focussed sharply instead of being fractionally off target, as they had often been before.

'Good evening.' He halted abruptly, taking in blankly the rather dishevelled appearance, the white, staring face of the girl in front of him. 'I'm afraid ...'

'Stein!' Suddenly she knew he hadn't guessed who she was, and, just as quickly, she noted Sophy's puzzled expression. Acting instinctively, she rushed over and grasped his arms, her eyes conveying a silent warning. 'I just got in an hour ago. I came as quickly as I could.'

Frantically she gazed at him, feeling his flesh tense beneath her fingers. It was all wrong! She should be asking how he was, telling him how glad she was to see him again, but it seemed imperative that Sophy shouldn't guess that he had never actually seen his wife before. Because naturally Sophy knew about Alexandra, about her having a part in Stein's film in America and, wasn't she, Sandra, supposed to be Alexandra?

As she spoke she saw Stein's face darken formidably and knew the nerve-racking sensation of his glance going wholly over her. It was so piercing she shrank back as his disappointment seemed obvious. 'My God,' he ground out, 'my wife! You took your time in getting here!'

There was no helpful clue as to whether he realised the extreme delicacy of the situation, or that he cared. How could she try to explain, plead her illness, when Sophy was standing gazing at them, her eyes full of a crafty curiosity? And what did Stein mean about her taking her time when he'd left explicit orders she wasn't to leave Corfu?

Then quickly, to Sandra's startled astonishment, it was Sophy who broke the frozen silence. 'I'm sorry, Stein,' she said smoothly, 'I don't feel like being relegated to the spare room. I think I'd better leave you until you get your affairs properly sorted out. You know where to find me.'

Completely dazed, Sandra watched as she disappeared into Stein's bedroom, emerging almost immediately with her suitcase. Had Sophy expected her action to bring Stein to an immediate decision, to throw his wife out?

'It's all here,' Sophy shrugged, her glance betraying nothing. 'I've flung everything in, but if I've left anything, Stein, just hang on to it.'

Vaguely aware of Stein's heavily spoken goodbye, Sandra contemplated the sharply closed door blankly. What did this all mean?

'Well,' Stein drawled, his face cold, 'that didn't take

long, did it? Now you've got rid of the one woman who seemed to really care about me, do you intend taking her place?'

Without waiting for a reply he turned, pushing open the lounge door, almost dragging her through it.

Because he seemed so indifferent, she cried, 'You don't appear to have taken any harm! Was she actually sleeping in your room?'

'Would you have cared if she had been?' he sneered, closing the door hard before crossing to the drinks cabinet in the corner.

'She knows about our divorce,' Sandra faltered, her voice, in spite of herself, echoing the pain in her heart.

'She could be guessing,' he replied flatly, pouring a large whisky.

'Oh!' Utterly confused, Sandra went off in another direction. 'She doesn't know you've never seen me before,' her voice shook. 'I told you you'd be disappointed. You thought I was a stranger!'

'Remember,' he challenged coolly, 'you were the last person I expected to see and, as you say, I hadn't ever seen you before. It wasn't until you spoke that I realised.'

What had he once said— 'I'd never mistake you, I don't need to see you.' How quickly he had forgotten!

Almost defiantly she stared into his dark face. 'You can see for yourself now how ordinary I am.'

'You aren't ordinary,' his mouth went tight. 'But I've learnt it's not as easy as I imagined to connect a voice with a body. Not that I've got it so very wrong. Maybe later to-night I'll tell you.'

'Stein,' her voice broke before the calculated determination in his, the way in which his eyes went discerningly over her, 'you know I can't stay here. If I do a divorce will become impossible.'

'You mean,' he taunted, 'you only came out of curiosity? God, I could have killed you!' With a bang which cracked it, he put down his empty glass and coming over grasped her shoulders, 'I wanted you beside me and I waited, but I knew you wouldn't turn up, you little fraud! While I was blind you thought you could lead me around by the nose, but the thought of a whole man frightens you.'

Her heart hardened as he called her names. Her appearance depressed him, but wasn't it better this should be so? It might make their parting that much easier, should he really believe her a fraud. What useful purpose would be served by telling him about her accident? None at all when he was so eager to think the worst of her.

Yet it wasn't easy to be indifferent, to subdue all the love and concern in her heart. There was so much she had to ask him. 'Please,' she faltered, 'now that I am here, can't we forget about everything else, at least for a little while? Can you really see?' her eyes roved over his, tears glinting on her cheeks, emphasising her anxiety. 'I didn't think you'd be out of hospital so soon and I've been so worried. You might not believe it, but I have been.'

'I would still be in hospital if they'd had their way,' he grunted, without removing his gaze from her anxious face. 'But I'm really quite all right,' he grinned derisively. 'I don't think I should be on my own, though, so you'd better be prepared to stay until I find someone else.'

'No, I can't!'

'Yes, you can!' Suddenly he hauled her up against him, his lips very close to her ear. 'You've a lot to make up for, my dear. You lied and cheated your way into my life and now you can really begin to pay for it. I can see again, Sandra, can look at what, so far, I've only been able to touch. I want time to see every little bit of you before I let you go.'

Gasping with dismay, she tried to pull away from him as his arms closed primitively around her. She mustn't listen to him! Wildly, through surging emotions, she uttered the best argument she could think of. 'How do you expect to get a divorce if you have me living here with you? What about Sophy?'

'What about her?' his voice mocked openly. 'By coming here tonight you've made an excellent job of chasing her away, but why should I allow this to deprive me of some feminine company? Do you think Sophy is really the kind of woman who'd be willing to live with me openly while I wait for a divorce? No, my small Sandra, it is you who will look after me until I fully recover. Then we will go abroad where, if one knows exactly how to go about it, a divorce may be obtained at almost the drop of a hat.'

Horrified, Sandra tried to twist from his iron grip. He hadn't the appearance of a man not fully recovered from anything! 'You must be mad,' she cried, 'if you think you can treat me this way!'

'You'd be mad to think I couldn't,' he sneered, his face harsh with determination as he held her suddenly away from him. With swift fingers he unbuttoned her shiny raincoat, sliding it from her shoulders and letting it drop to the floor. 'Now let me have a good look at you, girl. It's going to be quite interesting to discover if you match up exactly with how I imagined you would be.'

Sandra thought she would pass out before surviving his penetrating survey. His eyes were arrogant as they travelled over her slight body, which her recent spell in hospital and worry over him had made thin. 'You'll do,' his hands went curiously tense. 'You'll do very nicely indeed, especially when I find you something decent to wear.' His voice thickened as he bent his head and his lips brushed her soft mouth. 'You look younger than I'd expected, but that doesn't make you any less desirable. Right now I think I'd be a fool to turn you away.'

His mouth tasted of wine and warmth and promised rapture and she drew hastily away. His condescension hurt and she pushed against his hard arms.

'So you can scarcely bear me to touch you!' He let her

go curtly. 'I'll ring for dinner while you shower. Let's
hope you'll feel better after that. Put on something pretty.'

'But ...'

'For heaven's sake!' he ran an impatient hand round the
back of his neck. 'You'd better be prepared to indulge me.
I've had almost a year of darkness—I'd like something more
colourful for a change.'

Sandra showered quickly, imagining all the time that he
might come and disturb her. Some devil, a diabolic lean-
ing towards a subtle revenge for her seeming neglect, raged
in him. In his eyes she had committed an atrocity and must
be willing to pay for her deception. This she realised, but
had no clear idea how she was to defend herself. She had
only to feel his mouth on her own to have every iota of
common sense fly out of her head.

The shower relaxed her, yet she felt still strangely strung
up as she decided to please Stein by putting on the only
long dress she had brought with her. It was one she had
chosen for Kalnos, light and silky with a low neckline, a
neckline she had thought wouldn't matter when Stein
couldn't see her. Without thinking she had included it in
her luggage as it was the only one she hadn't worn several
times and, because it was light, wouldn't weigh too heavily
for air travel. Now it wouldn't have to matter if it made her
feel slightly unclothed.

Carefully, feeling she needed some extra defence, she
applied a sweep of mascara to her naturally thick lashes
and outlined her full, curved lips with a seductive gloss. Her
hair had grown longer as she had not had it cut while she
was away. After her accident it had grown lank, but she was
glad to see it beginning to shine again.

Once ready she waited, lingering a while in the room
Stein had shown her into. It was obviously the spare one
and, hoping to give every impression that she wanted to
remain here, she scattered her few belongings around.
When at last she dared hesitate no longer she took a deep
breath and went out.

Stein had changed, too, but just into a pair of dark slacks and thin shirt with a faint stripe to which he had added a tie. He was waiting in the dining room, along with dinner, and looked at her approvingly as she came towards him. Something smouldered at the back of his eyes as his glance touched the plunging neckline and his well shaped mouth quirked at the corners.

'A veritable swan,' he drawled, going forward to pull out her chair, his fingers lightly guiding on her bare back as he saw her seated.

As his fingers flicked fire through her she flinched, and feeling it he smiled grimly. 'As I said before, you don't seem able to bear me touching you.'

Sandra sat down too quickly, her long skirts tangling revealingly about her slender limbs. 'Why should I pretend otherwise when you can't wait to be rid of me?' She spoke with a calmness she was far from feeling.

'I'm not the only one in a hurry,' he muttered curtly, seating himself opposite, but because she wasn't sure if he referred to Sophy or herself, she kept silent.

Stein was paler, she saw, his face in repose darkly brooding, but just as attractive as ever. Throughout the meal she found it difficult to take her eyes off him. A miracle had given him back his sight, but it seemed she had to seek constant reassurance that it had really happened and that he was well.

Soon, in spite of the cool wariness between them, she was plying him with eager little questions about his operation, questions which seemed to come more readily as she drank the wine with which he kept replenishing her glass. Because it seemed to help, she drank recklessly, finding it curiously easier to drink than to eat the delicious food the restaurant supplied.

With a kind of forced tolerance Stein answered her many queries, his eyes seldom leaving her face. 'I had a rather special visitor at the clinic,' he said eventually.

'Who?' she swallowed hastily. 'You mean Sophy?'

'You already know about her.' His mouth twisted derisively, 'This other one—you'd never guess?'

'No—I couldn't.'

'Alexandra,' he smiled.

'Alexandra!' Sandra's green eyes widened with sudden fright. 'My—er—cousin?'

'Who else?'

'What did she want?' Sandra stared at him, her voice little more than a frightened whisper.

'Oh,' he shrugged, his quick glance taunting, 'she'd heard where I was.'

'Who told her? Was it the Professor?'

'No. He only stayed a few days before going on, but he had, I believe, mentioned it to mutual friends.'

'I see.' Sandra knew she had gone deathly pale. Yet another woman! What chance had she ever had? Of course Alexandra was married now. Or was she?

'Did she really marry Arnold?' she asked.

'Yes,' his broad shoulders lifted indifferently. 'She seems happy enough with her millions.'

'Did she mention me?'

'Now and then.' His eyes narrowed on her anxious face. 'You know Alexandra only likes talking about herself.'

Sandra's long lashes flickered miserably. So Alexandra hadn't told him the truth? Well, what did it matter now? Rashly she lifted her glass again. 'To all your past loves,' she laughed, her eyes bright with pain.

'To all the world's little deceivers,' he countered, raising his own glass, his mocking gaze sliding over her. 'To all the lovely wives who aren't there when they're needed.'

'Stein!' she protested, with a scarcely audible sob. 'You can't keep hurting me like this.'

'Can't I?' His lazy indolence immediately leaving him, he came around the table to pull her ruthlessly to her feet, almost thrusting her into the other room. 'You'll find I'm capable of much more than I used to be. Do you want coffee?'

'No!' she cried, hating him. He treated her as if she was of no account, as if he enjoyed tormenting her!

'I'll make it black,' his mouth curled. 'I could certainly do with some, if you can't.'

But making no attempt to set about making anything, he sat down beside her on the settee. He looked at her for a long time until, thoroughly unnerved, she felt on the point of screaming. He seemed to have a mocking need to examine every square inch of her. His hand went along the back of the cushion behind her, as if ready to follow the direction of his eyes as they rested on the pounding pulse at the base of her throat. He assumed an air of casualness, but there was a taut smile on his arrogant mouth. A swift shudder went through her as she wondered what he was thinking.

Time had flown, and she saw it was after nine. Uneasily she edged away from him, trying to ignore the dictates of her heart, to remember her pride. 'I think I'll have an early night, if you don't mind.'

'But I do mind.' His hand left the back of the settee to curve her shoulder, as he sought to detain her. 'Do you recall when you first sat on this settee? You stuttered and stammered so much I was intrigued.'

'I'd rather forget.' Her voice was curiously strangled as he examined the faint bruise he had made on her bare arm by dragging her here, and his mouth lowered to move softly over it.

'You'd rather forget too many things!' Suddenly he pulled her against him closely. 'But there are some I'm going to make sure you remember—for the rest of your life!'

His hand went firmly under her chin, tightening on the bone until her mouth came up to meet his. Her skin burned like fire as he began to kiss her until her lips felt numb from the hard pressure of his and her heart beat a frantic tattoo beneath his hand. She felt a suffocating warmth in her throat and a fine colour washed into her cheeks as he

slid the strap of her dress urgently to one side, so that he
might explore the satin smoothness of her shoulders.

'You're beautiful,' he muttered hoarsely, running his
hand down her narrow back as his lips crept down her neck
to kindle a devastating heat in her blood. His face lifted,
coming to rest with a groan against her own again. 'You're
so small and slender I could crush you. I could do it very
easily with wanting you so much.'

The touch of his mouth became an undeniable posses-
sion which had her arching herself almost shamelessly
against him as his lips continued their relentless pursual.
She knew he wanted her for, by this time, she was well
aware of the strength of his desire, but tonight there was
something else about him she couldn't fathom.

When at last he eased his grip a little, she whispered
brokenly, 'I don't know what you're trying to punish me
for now. Surely you can't keep remembering I pretended
to be Alexandra?'

'I've forgotten that long ago,' he said thickly, 'but I
still mean to have you.'

As his hands threaded cruelly through her tangled hair to
bring her face to the exact angle he wanted it, Sandra
stared up at him with shadowed eyes. Naked, unguarded
eyes. 'I don't know how you can talk, act this way when
you seem to love both Alexandra and Sophy.'

'Perhaps I never loved either,' his voice was full of self-
mockery. 'Maybe I was just trying to make you jealous, to
appease my ego by making you crawl.'

'Have you forgotten,' her face tautened, 'how you were
actually engaged to Alex before you even met me?'

He laughed, letting his hand slide over her hot cheek,
his eyes closely scanning her slightly gamine features, rest-
ing significantly on her passionate mouth. Pausing enigmatically, he said, 'I wonder if I should tell you, explain
just how much I loved Alexandra?'

'You don't have to!' Resentment flared that he should

expect her to endure such torture. Even though he didn't know how much she cared for him, she was his wife. 'Did you,' she accused, distraught, 'think of telling Alexandra we're married?'

'I believe I mentioned it,' he admitted coolly.

Her breath caught. Alex would hate her now. 'What did she say?' she faltered.

'Oh, quite a lot,' he laughed sarcastically. 'It was very obvious she considers you overreached yourself. Apparently marriage was not on the agreement when you agreed to stand in for her. She didn't appear to like it at all when I told her how very married we are.'

'Do you have to seek revenge all round? After all, Alexandra never did you any real harm—unless,' Sandra hesitated, her green eyes bright with unshed tears, 'you consider she did in foisting me on you?'

'I did initially,' he agreed cynically, as Sandra stared at him, wide-eyed and pale-cheeked. 'That was until I realised the fun I could be having at your expense—still intend having before I let you go and, believe me, it won't be as gentle as it has been before. When people hurt me I know how to hurt back!'

For an instant he sat glowering down at her with eyes that were darkly furious as he shook her slight shoulders before his mouth found hers in a wholly punishing kiss.

She fought him, as much as she fought the flame of scorching fire which went through her. No matter how savage, how cruel he was, something inside her responded fiercely. When she could no longer seem to bear it her hands clawed at his shoulders. Against his hard lips she gasped, 'If you don't let me go you'll be sorry!'

She had not expected to make any impression, and her small, desperate cry faded in surprise as suddenly she was free. Stein's arms dropped from her as his mouth tightened in disgust.

'I think I'd better make that coffee, after all.' His hand

brushed over his brow and down the back of his head, an unconscious gesture which Sandra had noticed previously. 'What the devil does a few days in hospital do to a man!' he grunted darkly. 'Or maybe I should have stayed longer.'

Following him through to the kitchenette, Sandra saw he was white beneath his tan, but he plugged in the percolator and watched it grimly. She felt her own face pale anxiously as she read the signs of strain. Stein's was normally a strength above average and even to feel a little weak disgusted him. He would hate to think he was in any way vulnerable. Of course he should still have been in hospital.

'Hadn't you better sit down?' Alarm shook her voice and, while she might have looked on this interlude as a kind of reprieve, her love for him was such that she could only consider his pain. 'Stein, you look shaken ...'

'Maybe,' he retorted curtly, 'it has more to do with you than my actual health.'

This hadn't occurred to her, but somehow she couldn't believe it. Bewildered she shook her head, 'But you've just had a bad operation!'

'Oh, that,' he shrugged indifferently. 'The condition of my eyes wasn't nearly as bad as it could have been. I guess I was one of the lucky ones, so you can save your soft little glances for someone else. My eyes just need a little time. You weren't to know, of course.'

Abruptly he pulled out a chair, slumping down on it against the table. 'See how the mighty are fallen,' he quipped. 'You should enjoy it! Maybe,' he growled, as she went swiftly to the lounge and returned with some brandy, 'Maybe I've been trying to do too much too soon, but you make me see red every time I look at you.'

He swallowed the brandy in one gulp, then grasped her wrist so suddenly that she half stumbled, catching her elbow on the side of the table as he pulled her down to him. He didn't apologise, not even on hearing her small cry of pain. He looked impervious if anything. 'I thought you were beginning to love me,' he jeered. 'I thought I could feel it in my bones, the way you responded to me each time I made love to you. You held nothing back, did you?' Rage tightened his mouth to a thin line and the paleness of his face was suffused by a dull red. 'I can still feel how you used to be in my arms, how you could make me want you until I feared I might kill you. But as soon as I was gone you forgot about me. Your ghost haunted my hospital bed while you stayed on Corfu, enjoying yourself.'

'Stein ...' Her eyes heavy with misery, Sandra felt herself shaken by a strange shuddering as she stared into his contemptuous face, sensing the anger which, like a living thing, was tearing through him. Suddenly she knew what she must do. There was a deadlock to break and she must be the one to make the first move. Stein was proud and so, she had discovered, was she, but where was pride going to get either of them? Wasn't it foolish to withhold the truth in the futile hope that he would suddenly realise something traumatic must have kept her from coming to him? She had never told him of her love, circumstances having been stacked against such a confession, and he obviously had not guessed.

She could see now that, because he was so used to being absolutely in control of every situation, he had needed the assurance of her flying immediately to his side. What he had hoped to gain from this she couldn't think. Or was it that she didn't dare hope?

'Stein,' again her voice faltered, but this time she forced herself to go on, 'do you really want to know why I didn't follow you over here straight away?'

He went quite still, the only visible movement the tensing of a muscle in his hard jaw. 'I don't want to hear any more fictitious stories,' he warned coldly.

'I had an accident,' she confessed starkly, trying to ignore his rough words. 'On our way to the airport on Corfu, Thimios met another car and we crashed. I was in hospital over a week with concussion—until they checked everything was all right, you know. After I got out I came here as soon as I was able. At least,' she hesitated, knowing this wasn't exactly the whole truth, 'I might have come a day or two sooner, but I seemed to have lost what little confidence I had. I wasn't sure, you see, that you'd welcome me. In that note you left you were quite adamant about not wanting me. It was your grandmother who actually persuaded me to come.'

If Stein had listened to this in grim silence, he came alive as her voice broke unhappily. He went pale again, his fingers tightening dangerously about her wrist. 'Why didn't you tell me?' he rasped furiously. 'Why the hell didn't someone else tell me if you couldn't? You mean to say you were actually injured and in hospital and no one thought to let me know?'

Sandra could only see his anger, not the hard tension behind it. She could have complained a lot about his grandmother, but there seemed little sense in doing so now. Now that the old lady seemed kinder perhaps eventually they could be friends. 'We didn't want you worried,' she said quickly. 'It was important that this shouldn't happen and your grandmother insisted there could be disastrous results. The funny thing was,' her voice faltered miserably, 'I could have told her you wouldn't have been so worried, because you didn't love me. At least, not as I love you.'

'Sandra!' he began angrily. Then, as if just realising what she had said, he exclaimed hoarsely, 'Would you please repeat that? That last bit?'

Feeling numb, she complied listlessly. She hadn't meant to let it slip out, but now it didn't seem to matter. 'I love you.'

'How long?' he asked unsteadily, never taking his eyes from her desolate face.

'Before I married you,' she whispered, through stiff lips.

'If I hadn't loved you I don't think I could have gone through with it.'

'But you kept it to yourself all this time,' he accused her harshly. 'You little ...'

'Don't say it!' Suddenly she was sobbing wildly, tears streaming down her cheeks. 'I don't love you any more. I think I hate you! What do you want me to do? You've had me grovelling, in about every way you could think of, yet you still aren't satisfied!'

'Oh, darling!' His expression changed, but his eyes were still dark with angry passion as he drew her closer, kissing her wet eyes, her softly childish mouth. 'I'm sorry! But when I think of the time we've wasted! On Kalnos I tried to resist you but couldn't. I know I had no real excuse for making love to you that night you believed the lights had failed, but things got beyond my control. You don't have any idea of the agony I suffered at the clinic. Not because of my op, but because I imagined you didn't want to come to me. To know now that you care, even half as much as I love you, is scarcely believable.'

'Stein!' As he paused thickly she had only time to utter his name before he kissed her gently. Then, as he lifted her and carried her into his bedroom, their lips came together violently as he crushed her against him. He laid her on the wide bed and between disjointed words his mouth found hers blindly, as if he never wanted to be free of it. This time she was a willing captive and, as he made urgent love to her, she was content to be borne along on a wave of earth-shattering sensation. She could only cling to him as he undressed her, then everything around her seemed to dissolve beneath the weight of his passionate desire. When their emotions combined to reach a devastating climax she felt she was at the heart of a whirlwind, lost, helpless and entirely possessed.

Later, as they lay together, he rested his head against her warm breast and said soberly, 'I love you, my darling—

don't ever think you'll be free of me now. I didn't guess you loved me and I wanted you to suffer a little—as I was doing. That's why I wrote that note, why I kept on about a divorce—I fancied it got under your skin. But, most of all, I hoped you'd follow me over here almost at once. That, I decided, would prove you cared more than you realised. Imagine my thoughts when you didn't turn up! My pride as well as my heart suffered a severe blow. That was why I wouldn't speak to you on the telephone, why I didn't seem particularly pleased to see you when you did arrive. I didn't count on holding out long, though—not when I realised my heart was suffering most of all. In fact I was desperately fighting a losing battle when you told me you loved me.'

Entirely content, she snuggled deeper into his arms as he held her and caressed her. 'You don't still want to get rid of me?'

'No!' His hand tightened painfully on her waist in mock threat. 'Just try getting away from me! Don't you think,' he growled, nuzzling her cheek, 'I need a wife to help me through my convalescence?'

'What about all your other loving women?' she teased, then found herself sighing. 'You were going to tell me about Alexandra once. You must have loved her?'

He lifted his head, half frowning before suddenly smiling at her. 'Ah, yes, the story of your cousin. Obviously she never told you how we became engaged?'

'She did say you rescued her from an unwanted admirer.'

'And foolishly, my dear, offered her the temporary protection of an engagement ring. Strictly a business arrangement, mind you. This was when this chap continued to torment her. I felt sorry for her, and we seemed to be having enough problems with the film without inviting more. The snag came when she refused to keep her side of the bargain, to break the engagement off. Which seemed crazy as we were not even slightly in love with each other. I couldn't recall ever kissing her. She babbled a lot about the humiliation she would suffer if I was to leave her. Quite frankly I thought she'd taken leave of her senses and gave her a few days to think it over.

'This was when the accident happened in which I was blinded. I went back, but she still refused to release me and I lost my temper. I flung out after a furious row and didn't see another car shoot out of a side-road. The other man was drunk and in the wrong, but I was the one who got hurt.'

Staring up at him, Sandra drew a shocked breath, horrified yet not too surprised at Alexandra's incredible behaviour. Her cousin had always been highly strung and unpredictable. 'I'm sorry, Stein,' she said helplessly. 'What did Alexandra do then?'

He shrugged wryly. 'Oh, she came around, drooling tears and making the most of the publicity, and for a while I was too ill to care. When I did recover I pretended, to my shame, that my blindness was more permanent than my doctors had given me to believe. Only that didn't help to get rid of her either. I didn't guess that, around this time, she met Arnold, but instead of telling me, she began suffering from an outsize conscience where I was concerned. That was why, she's since confessed, she agreed to learn typing and to come with me to Corfu, but when Arnold objected I think she got in a terrible panic and flew for you.'

'I really believe she must love Arnold very much,' Sandra sighed. Wrapped closely in Stein's arms she felt she could afford to be generous.

Stein grinned dryly. 'More likely his bank balance was the big attraction, especially compared to that of a disabled writer. However, as she sent me you, I'm prepared to forgive her.'

Uneasily Sandra stirred. 'I must have seemed slightly ridiculous, trying to step into her shoes.'

'Yes, my dear, you did! And I admit to being furious with your family all over again. I was even more furious when you suceeded in entwining yourself around my heart.

Every day I seemed to be falling more in love with you.'

'Do you regret it?' Sandra dared ask.

He smiled slightly as he shook his dark head, 'No. I haven't since I first kissed you, right here in this flat. It was then that I knew you weren't Alexandra, but that I couldn't let you go. Which proved ironical, my darling, when I'd been searching for weeks for a means of getting rid of Alexandra. It was an unbelievable experience, falling in love with a girl I'd never seen. But you're lovely, my small Sandra, more beautiful than I ever imagined you would be. When my intuition told me who you were, this afternoon, I could scarcely believe it.'

'Flatterer!' Sandra teased, yet couldn't hide her pleasure that she pleased him. 'So you'll forgive me too?'

'Yes, but you must send back the money Alexandra gave you.'

'But I never had it,' Sandra said blankly. 'I believe I was to see Arnold's solicitors, but I never even picked up the address. It was only because of the utterly callous way Alexandra seemed to be treating you that I agreed to do as she asked—and,' she hesitated, adding unhappily, trying to be completely honest, 'and because Gran had just died and I was broke as well as untrained.'

'Sandra!' He brushed his lips tenderly over hers. 'I don't want you to upset yourself about it now. It's all over. Alexandra did confess a lot last week, after I told her how much I loved you. If it will make you any happier you can tell me the little bits she undoubtedly left out, later. Right now I don't want to talk any more about other women.'

'Not even Sophy?'

'Not even Sophy,' he mocked, his dark eyes meeting Sandra's pleading ones sternly. 'But, rather than have you worried, I might just mention that she stayed here, rather than go to a hotel, while I was in the clinic. She was actually packed, ready to leave, when you arrived. She had no intention of remaining here with me, in spite of her rather devious remarks. She's much too fond of her immaculate reputation.'

'Oh, darling!' Sandra breathed, and it was a while before he would allow her to speak again.

Eventually he murmured against her hot cheek, 'I'm no millionaire, darling. Much as I love you, you might have to be prepared to live more or less permanently on Kalnos, and I wasn't altogether kind to you there. Unfortunately my occupation tends to be rather precarious, but we'll always have the island.'

'I'll be happy with you anywhere,' she promised, 'as long as you're content.'

'If I have you and Kalnos and the precious gift of my sight to see you both, what more could a man want? If that will be enough for you?'

'You'd be enough without anything else,' she assured him softly, winding her arms around him, holding him closer. Her lips curved as his touched them. 'I think I would be willing to do anything if you just keep on loving me.'

'That's something I'll never tire of doing,' he threatened, and for a long time everything but their own need of each other was forgotten.

**Harlequin Presents...**

The beauty of true romance...
The excitement of world travel...
The splendor of first love...

# unique love stories for today's woman

Harlequin Presents...
novels of honest,
twentieth-century love,
with characters who
are interesting, vibrant
and alive.

The elegance of love...
The warmth of romance...
The lure of faraway places...

Six new novels, every
month — wherever
paperbacks are sold.

# Harlequin brings you a book to cherish ...

three stories of
love and romance
by one of your
favorite
Harlequin authors ...